FROM SOUTHERN GARDEN

Louisiana Gardening Planner 2023

Louisiana month by month edible garden planner and
reference guide for abundant harvests and self-sufficiency.

THIS BOOK BELONGS TO:

_____

_____

_____

_____

ISBN: 978-1-946050-25-0
Louisiana Gardening Planner 2023
Louisiana month by month edible garden planner and
reference guide for abundant harvests and self-
sufficiency. ©2022 by Southern Garden
Published by Garden Gateway Press
An imprint of
Vagabondage Press LLC
PO Box 3563
Apollo Beach, Florida 33572
http://www.southerngarden.net

INTRODUCTION

More people than ever have taken up gardening in the last two years. For some, it has been a welcome distraction from lockdowns and isolation orders. For others, gardening has become an important hedge against inflation, helping to fill gaps in the menu and grocery budget due to rising food costs and shortages. And for many, it has rekindled a need to stay connected to the natural world.

Maybe for you, it has been a little of all three of these things.

But gardening can be overwhelming, especially when you want to grow everything you can in your backyard. It can be even more overwhelming in the South, where seasons are extended, and the weather becomes increasingly unpredictable.

If you're new to gardening or new to gardening in the South and you've already lost your vegetable plots to summer storms and heat waves and plagues of insects, you're not alone. Many new Louisiana gardeners have suffered the same losses.

I planted my first garden in the South in 1993, and it failed so miserably that I didn't try again until 20 years later. I finally discovered why it was so difficult and why my previous successes up north meant nothing. I discovered the secret—and it's the same secret that every successful gardener knows:

Right plant, right place.

But the real secret for those of us in the steamy southern states is that there's one more dimension to that old adage: *Right time.*

You really can garden year-round in Louisiana and produce a bountiful harvest of fresh, delicious, and nutritious fruits and vegetables. As long as you know what you can plant, and even more importantly, when to plant it.

Our Louisiana gardening planner offers easy-to-use charts of what to plant when, along with resources that will help you achieve better variety and more nutrition from your garden. You may find yourself becoming more self-sufficient too.

Take advantage of Louisiana's climate to create your own backyard paradise that will keep you healthy and well-fed, both physically and mentally.

Welcome to gardening in the South!

HOW TO USE THIS PLANNER

The 2023 edition of the Southern Garden Louisiana Gardening Planner starts in January of 2023 and runs to December 2023. While fall is a good time for new gardeners to find success in Louisiana, the spring growing season gets into gear in January when many gardeners start their seeds indoors for planting out when the weather warms.

PLANNING TOOLS

First, you'll find a year-at-a-glance calendar, which you can use for long-term planning throughout the whole year.

The monthly calendar sheets follow, so you can add appointments and events. This will allow you to coordinate major gardening tasks with work and family obligations. It's also a good place to note projects that will take several weeks to complete.

Then, for each month, you'll find a list of the best edible plants to get started or plant out for each month of the year. These are then divided in the two separate zones for the state: North and South Louisiana.

For the most part, these two regions should be a good guide to when you should start seeds and plant out vegetables. However, many coastal areas in Louisiana can run to warmer temperatures and may be designated Zone 10a by the USDA. This usually means that you can sow your seeds or plant out your starter plants two or three weeks earlier than other parts of South Louisiana.

You can find your growing zone more accurately by visiting the USDA site at https://planthardiness.ars.usda.gov/.

If you're on the border of two zones, try experimenting with both sides of those dividing lines. You may find you can plant later or earlier than you thought.

After the monthly growing guide, we've added weekly planning sheets so you can stay on top of regular garden chores as well as plan when to sow seeds or plant out starters.

Because one of the keys to successful gardening in the South is succession planning, we've added garden plot grids for each month of the year. This will allow you to keep track of the next empty spot in your garden. That way, you can sow starter plants in advance and plant out well-developed seedlings in four to eight weeks when the space opens up.

UNDERSTANDING PLANT CHARTS

For each zone, you'll find recommendations for starting various vegetable plants, and they're listed as "start indoors," "direct sow," or "plant out starts."

Starting Indoors

During months when the weather is extreme, some vegetables should be started indoors. This allows them a chance to become well established before being exposed to the elements. You can start them in cell trays, soil blocks, or small pots.

The weather changes quickly and radically in the South, so starting many vegetables indoors allows you to take advantage of the first days of the growing season.

In the winter months, you'll want to protect them from cold snaps, when temperatures plummet and cold fronts bring harsh winds that can burn them. In summer months, you'll need to protect them from heavy rains and wind damage from storms.

Starting these plants indoors means you can better control the temperature and moisture levels. You can move them outdoors when the weather is warm and sunny, and then bring them indoors when it's cold or raining heavily.

After hardening off, you can plant them outdoors after four to six weeks if temperatures are suitable and the plants have developed enough to withstand the elements. Most vegetables will be ready to plant out in four to eight weeks, once they have a full set of true leaves. Some plants, such as eggplants, peppers, and tomatoes, can be started as much as 10 to 12 weeks before planting out, although you will need to ensure you have a large enough pot to accommodate them. Plants marked with an asterisk (*) may need 12 to 16 weeks or more to develop before planting out.

Direct Sowing

Many vegetable plants prefer direct sowing. This is because they grow quickly and will outgrow most cell trays before becoming well developed. They may also need to put down deep tap roots to flourish and growing these plants in cell trays results in stunted plants that don't produce.

During months when temperatures are mild and storm activity is at a lull, usually mid-spring and late fall, most vegetable can be direct sown in good soil. You may decide to direct sow plants that are otherwise marked to start indoors. It's okay to experiment, as long as you keep an eye on the forecast.

Plant Out Starts

Some vegetable plants in these charts are marked as "plant out starts." In this case, many of them are not grown from seed by most home gardeners. They're often propagated from cuttings or purchased from a nursery. For example, many of the tropical spinaches are grown from cuttings, so we haven't included times to sow them from seed. It also includes strawberry plants, which are very difficult to grow from seed in hot climates, and normally purchased as bare roots or established plants.

LOGGING TOOLS

In order to help you better track what works and what doesn't work in your garden, we've included some logging tools.

First, we've included a harvest tracker for each month of the year. If you've ever watched gardening videos, you may have seen many gardeners adding up the pounds of food they've grown. You can keep track of your own fruit and vegetable hauls on the harvest tracking sheet.

Another of the best-held gardening secrets is that variety matters—especially in in the South. Some tomato types might be more resistant to one of our many diseases. There are varieties of broccoli that can more easily tolerate our heat than those grown up north.

To help you track the varieties that work best in your garden, we have included annual edible plant logs where you can record which plants and varieties you planted and how well they performed. That way, you'll know which varieties are your go-to types in years to come.

Likewise, we included sheets to record your perennial plantings, such as fruit trees and berry bushes. Both types of logs will help you track the plants' light, water, and fertilization requirements, as well as their growth over time.

Finally, we have logs where you can jot down your contact list and record the nurseries, seed sellers, and landscapers you prefer. Why take chances with an unknown vendor when you can do business with a trusted source?

NEW RESOURCES

We've added a few extra tips and tricks this year that we hope will help new gardeners and those who are new to gardening in the state.

Along with charts for planting vegetables and fruits, we've added schedules for planting out flowering plants for pollinators. Bees, butterflies, and even wasps do a critical job for gardeners by providing pollination and even some pest control services. So, for any successful garden, it pays to plant flowers to attract more of them to your yard.

Included, you'll also find a list of the best varieties of fruit and vegetable plants that have a proven track record of growing well in Louisiana. These are varieties recommended by state extension offices, professional growers, and from personal experience.

Next, we offer an easy-to-read chart of germination temperature requirements for many common seeds. This will help you pinpoint your timing if you're not confident about sowing your seeds directly into the garden.

Also new for 2023 is a handy list of the first and last frost dates for Louisiana gardeners, so you can reference them quickly when planning your garden.

If you ever have a question or suggestion for the Garden Planner, please reach out. Your feedback is critical to helping us all grow a better, more diverse, and healthier Louisiana.

To learn more about gardening in Louisiana and other Southern states, check out our website at SouthernGarden.net. You can also visit our mobile site by scanning the QR code below with your smartphone camera:

TABLE OF CONTENTS

Annual Gardening Planner 2023

January	February	March

April	May	June

July	August	September

October	November	December

Gardening Goals for 2023

_____ ☐

_____ ☐

_____ ☐

_____ ☐

_____ ☐

JANUARY

NORTH LOUISIANA / ZONE 8

Start Indoors			Direct Sow	
beets bok choy broccoli cabbage Cape gooseberry	Chinese cabbage chives* cilantro kale kohlrabi	mitsuba parsley spinach Swiss chard tatsoi	bok choy carrots collards dill endive leeks	lettuce mizuna onion sets parsnip peas shallots

SOUTH LOUISIANA / ZONE 9

Start Indoors		Direct Sow		Plant Out Starts
bok choy broccoli cabbage Chinese cabbage chives* cilantro	kale mitsuba parsley spinach Swiss chard tatsoi	beets carrots collards dill endive Irish potatoes lettuce	onion sets peas radish rutabaga shallots turnips	cauliflower celeriac/celery kohlrabi

FLOWERING POLLINATOR PLANTS FOR JANUARY

Sow Seeds or Plant Starts

North Louisiana / Zone 8		South Louisiana / Zone 9	
asters bee balm dianthus lavender	pansies petunias snapdragon violas	agapanthus asters bee balm crinum lily	dianthus pansies petunias snapdragons

Monthly Garden Tip:

January in Louisiana often brings sudden overnight cold snaps that will kill tender plants. You can protect plants when night temperatures drop below 35°F with a few simple steps.

Water thoroughly at the base of each plant the day before a cold snap and mulch deeply around the root zone. Before sunset, cover plants completely from the top to the ground with cloth covers to keep in warmth.

Make sure to remove the covers when the sun comes up the next day.

January 2023

Sunday	Monday	Tuesday	Wednesday	Thursday	Friday	Saturday
1	2	3	4	5	6	7
8	9	10	11	12	13	14
15	16	17	18	19	20	21
22	23	24	25	26	27	28
29	30	31	1	2	3	4

December

12/26/22 - 01/01/23

○ 26. MONDAY

Garden Jobs for the Week

_____

_____

_____

○ 27. TUESDAY

_____

_____

_____

_____

○ 28. WEDNESDAY

To Sow / Plant / Propagate

_____

_____

○ 29. THURSDAY

_____

_____

_____

_____

○ 30. FRIDAY

_____

_____

_____

_____

○ 31. SATURDAY / 1. SUNDAY

_____

_____

_____

_____

January

Week 1   01/02/23 - 01/08/23

○ 2. MONDAY

Garden Jobs for the Week

_____

_____

○ 3. TUESDAY

_____

_____

_____

_____

_____

○ 4. WEDNESDAY

To Sow / Plant / Propagate

_____

_____

○ 5. THURSDAY

_____

_____

_____

_____

_____

○ 6. FRIDAY

_____

_____

_____

_____

_____

○ 7. SATURDAY / 8. SUNDAY

_____

_____

_____

_____

January

○ 9. MONDAY

Garden Jobs for the Week

_____

_____

_____

○ 10. TUESDAY

_____

_____

_____

○ 11. WEDNESDAY

To Sow / Plant / Propagate

_____

_____

○ 12. THURSDAY

_____

_____

_____

_____

○ 13. FRIDAY

_____

_____

_____

_____

○ 14. SATURDAY / 15. SUNDAY

_____

_____

_____

_____

January

Week 3   01/16/23 - 01/22/23

○ 16. MONDAY

Garden Jobs for the Week

_____
_____
_____
○ 17. TUESDAY
_____
_____
_____
_____
_____

○ 18. WEDNESDAY

To Sow / Plant / Propagate

_____
_____
_____
○ 19. THURSDAY
_____
_____
_____
_____
_____

○ 20. FRIDAY

_____
_____
_____
_____
_____
○ 21. SATURDAY / 22. SUNDAY
_____
_____
_____
_____

January

Week 4   01/23/23 - 01/29/23

○ 23. MONDAY

Garden Jobs for the Week

_____

_____

_____

○ 24. TUESDAY

_____

_____

_____

_____

○ 25. WEDNESDAY

To Sow / Plant / Propagate

_____

_____

○ 26. THURSDAY

_____

_____

_____

_____

○ 27. FRIDAY

_____

_____

_____

_____

○ 28. SATURDAY / 29. SUNDAY

_____

_____

_____

January

Week 5

01/30/23 - 02/05/23

○ 30. MONDAY

Garden Jobs for the Week

_____

_____

_____

○ 31. TUESDAY

_____

_____

_____

_____

_____

○ 1. WEDNESDAY

To Sow / Plant / Propagate

_____

_____

○ 2. THURSDAY

_____

_____

_____

_____

_____

○ 3. FRIDAY

_____

_____

_____

_____

_____

○ 4. SATURDAY / 5. SUNDAY

_____

_____

_____

_____

FEBRUARY

NORTH LOUISIANA / ZONE 8

Start Indoors			Direct Sow or Plant Out Starts		
bok choy	chives*	Swiss chard	arugula	Irish potatoes	radish
broccoli	cilantro	tatsoi	beets	kale	rutabaga
cabbage	mitsuba	tomatoes	cardoon	kohlrabi	shallots
cauliflower	parsley	watermelon	carrots	lettuce	spinach
celeriac/celery	peppers, chili	winter savory*	collards	mustard	sunchokes
Chinese cabbage	pumpkins		dill	onion sets	turnips
			endive	peas	

SOUTH LOUISIANA / ZONE 9

Start Indoors		Direct Sow		Plant Out Starts
bok choy	Mexican tarragon	amaranth, grain	kale	cauliflower
broccoli	mitsuba	arugula	lettuce	celeriac/celery
cabbage	New Zealand spinach	beans, bush	lovage	kohlrabi
cantaloupe	okra	beets	mirliton/chayote	
Chinese cabbage	oregano*	borage	mitsuba	
chives*	parsley	carrots	mustard	
cilantro	peppers, sweet	collards	radish	
cucumbers	rosemary	comfrey	rutabaga	
cucuzza	squash, summer	corn, sweet	shallots	
cumin	squash, winter	dill	spinach	
eggplant	Swiss chard	endive	sunflower	
fennel	tatsoi	ginger	turmeric	
honeydew	tomatillo	horseradish crowns	turnips	
luffa	tomatoes	Irish potatoes		
marjoram*	watermelon			

FLOWERING POLLINATOR PLANTS FOR FEBRUARY

Sow Seeds or Plant Starts

North Louisiana / Zone 8		South Louisiana / Zone 9		
agapanthus	lavender	asters	lobelia	snapdragons
asters	nigella	bee balm	melampodium	strawflower
bee balm	pansies	calendula	nasturtiums	sunflowers
crinum lily	pansy	cornflower	nicotiana	tithonia
dahlia bulbs	snapdragons	crossandra	nigella	verbena
dianthus	viola	dianthus	pansies	
		gerbera daisies	petunias	

Monthly Garden Tip:

Cool, dry February weather offers Louisiana gardeners the perfect opportunity to improve the infrastructure in their gardens.

Add trellises and other supports to keep climbing plants like cucumbers and melons off the ground and free from disease. Install drip lines or soaker hoses while garden beds are empty to maximize watering efficiency in coming growing seasons.

February 2023

Sunday	Monday	Tuesday	Wednesday	Thursday	Friday	Saturday
29	30	31	1	2	3	4
5	6	7	8	9	10	11
12	13	14	15	16	17	18
19	20	21	22	23	24	25
26	27	28	1	2	3	4

February

Week 6   02/06/23 - 02/12/23

○ 6. MONDAY

Garden Jobs for the Week

○ 7. TUESDAY

○ 8. WEDNESDAY

To Sow / Plant / Propagate

○ 9. THURSDAY

○ 10. FRIDAY

○ 11. SATURDAY / 12. SUNDAY

February

○ 13. MONDAY

Garden Jobs for the Week

○ 14. TUESDAY

○ 15. WEDNESDAY

To Sow / Plant / Propagate

○ 16. THURSDAY

○ 17. FRIDAY

○ 18. SATURDAY / 19. SUNDAY

February

Week 8   02/20/23 - 02/26/23

○ 20. MONDAY

Garden Jobs for the Week

_____

_____

_____

○ 21. TUESDAY

_____

_____

_____

_____

○ 22. WEDNESDAY

To Sow / Plant / Propagate

_____

_____

_____

○ 23. THURSDAY

_____

_____

_____

_____

_____

_____

○ 24. FRIDAY

_____

_____

_____

_____

_____

○ 25. SATURDAY / 26. SUNDAY

_____

_____

_____

_____

_____

February

Week 9   02/27/23 - 03/05/23

○ 27. MONDAY

Garden Jobs for the Week

_____
_____
_____
○ 28. TUESDAY
_____
_____
_____
_____
_____

○ 1. WEDNESDAY

To Sow / Plant / Propagate

_____
_____
_____
○ 2. THURSDAY
_____
_____
_____
_____
_____
○ 3. FRIDAY
_____
_____
_____
_____
_____
○ 4. SATURDAY / 5. SUNDAY
_____
_____
_____
_____

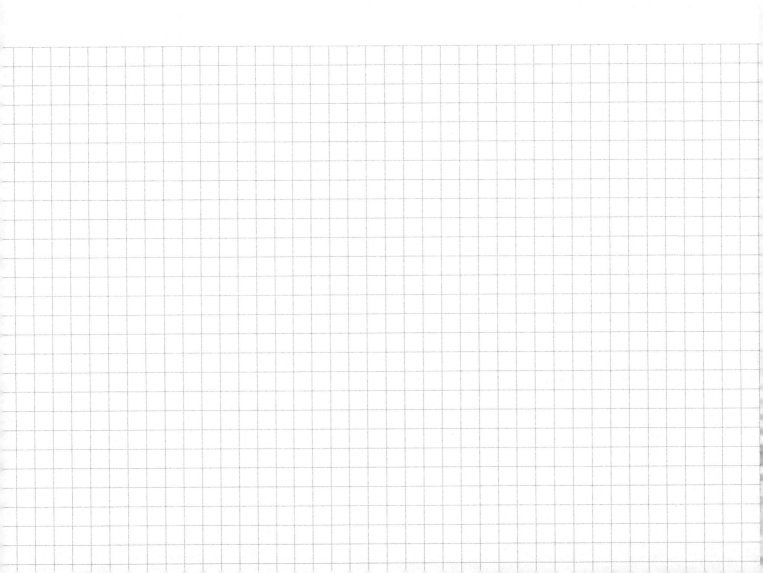

Harvest Tracker

Month _____

Year _____

Day															Total
1															
2															
3															
4															
5															
6															
7															
8															
9															
10															
11															
12															
13															
14															
15															
16															
17															
18															
19															
20															
21															
22															
23															
24															
25															
26															
27															
28															
29															
30															
31															

MARCH

NORTH LOUISIANA / ZONE 8

Direct Sow or Plant Out Starts			Direct Sow			Plant Out Starts
amaranth, grain	lemon balm	pumpkins	arugula	corn, sweet	mustard	bok choy
broccoli	luffa	rosemary	asparagus crowns	dill	radish	cabbage
celeriac/celery	marjoram*	squash, summer	beans, bush	endive	rutabaga	cauliflower
cilantro	mint	squash, winter	beans, climbing	ginger	spinach	Chinese cabbage
cucumbers	mitsuba	Swiss chard	beets	honeydew	summer savory	horseradish crowns
cucuzza	New Zealand spinach	tomatillo	borage	Irish potatoes	sunchokes	kohlrabi
cumin	okra	tomatoes	cantaloupe	kale	sunflower	longevity spinach
cushaw	oregano*	watermelon	cardoon	lettuce	taro	Okinawa spinach
eggplant	parsley	winter savory*	carrots	lovage	turmeric	tatsoi
fennel	peppers, chili		collards	malanga	turnips	
French tarragon	peppers, sweet		comfrey	mirliton/chayote	water chestnuts	

SOUTH LOUISIANA / ZONE 9

Start Indoors			Direct Sow			Plant Out Starts
basil	marjoram*	rosemary	amaranth, grain	ginger	radish	arrowroot
cucumbers	Mexican tarragon	squash, summer	arugula	horseradish crowns	rutabaga	bok choy
cucuzza	mint	squash, winter	asparagus crowns	Irish potatoes	spinach	broccoli
cumin	moringa*	Swiss chard	beans, bush	jicama	summer savory	cabbage
cushaw	New Zealand spinach	tomatillo	beets	kale	sunflower	cantaloupe
eggplant	oregano*	tomatoes	boniato slips	lettuce	taro	celeriac/celery
fennel	peppers, chili	watermelon	carrots	lovage	turmeric	Chinese cabbage
lemon balm	peppers, sweet		collards	malanga	water chestnuts	honeydew
luffa	pumpkins		comfrey	mirliton/chayote	yacon tubers	hops
			corn, sweet	mustard	yam tubers	kohlrabi
			daikon	okra		longevity spinach
			dill	papalo/quilquina		Okinawa spinach
						tatsoi
						tindora

FLOWERING POLLINATOR PLANTS FOR MARCH

Sow Seeds or Plant Starts

North Louisiana / Zone 8			South Louisiana / Zone 9		
African daisies	crossandra	melampodium	African daisies	cosmos	melampodium
Angelonia	dahlia bulbs	nasturtiums	Angelonia	crossandra	nasturtiums
asters	dianthus	nigella	asters	dahlia bulbs	nigella
cornflower	gerberas daisies	nicotiana	cornflower	daylily bulbs	phlox
bee balm	lavender	pansies	bee balm	gaillardia	tithonia
calendula	lobelia	snapdragons	Bulbine	gazania	salvias
		sunflowers	calendula	gerbera daisies	sunflowers
		viola	cleome	lobelia	zinnias
		zinnias	coleus	marigolds	

Monthly Garden Tip:

March is one of the busiest gardening months of the year in Louisiana, but it's also one of the driest. Don't forget that your small seedlings have undeveloped roots and can't quite reach the water deep in the ground.

Moisten directly sown seeds daily until germination occurs and then as needed. Water transplants daily for the first 5 to 7 days until they become established and produce new growth. However, avoid over-watering seedlings that are still in their cell trays to prevent dampening off.

March 2023

Sunday	Monday	Tuesday	Wednesday	Thursday	Friday	Saturday
26	27	28	1	2	3	4
5	6	7	8	9	10	11
12	13	14	15	16	17	18
19	20	21	22	23	24	25
26	27	28	29	30	31	1

March

Week 10   03/06/23 - 03/12/23

○ 6. MONDAY

Garden Jobs for the Week

○ 7. TUESDAY

○ 8. WEDNESDAY

To Sow / Plant / Propagate

○ 9. THURSDAY

○ 10. FRIDAY

○ 11. SATURDAY / 12. SUNDAY

March

Week 11   03/13/23 - 03/19/23

○ 13. MONDAY

Garden Jobs for the Week

_____

_____

○ 14. TUESDAY

_____

_____

_____

_____

_____

○ 15. WEDNESDAY

To Sow / Plant / Propagate

_____

_____

○ 16. THURSDAY

_____

_____

_____

_____

_____

○ 17. FRIDAY

_____

_____

_____

_____

_____

○ 18. SATURDAY / 19. SUNDAY

_____

_____

_____

_____

March

Week 12   03/20/23 - 03/26/23

○ 20. MONDAY

Garden Jobs for the Week

○ 21. TUESDAY

○ 22. WEDNESDAY

To Sow / Plant / Propagate

○ 23. THURSDAY

○ 24. FRIDAY

○ 25. SATURDAY / 26. SUNDAY

March

Week 13 03/27/23 - 04/02/23

○ 27. MONDAY

Garden Jobs for the Week

_____

_____

_____

○ 28. TUESDAY

_____

_____

_____

_____

○ 29. WEDNESDAY

To Sow / Plant / Propagate

_____

_____

○ 30. THURSDAY

_____

_____

_____

_____

_____

○ 31. FRIDAY

_____

_____

_____

_____

○ 1. SATURDAY / 2. SUNDAY

_____

_____

_____

_____

Harvest Tracker

Month _____

Year _____

Day															Total
1															
2															
3															
4															
5															
6															
7															
8															
9															
10															
11															
12															
13															
14															
15															
16															
17															
18															
19															
20															
21															
22															
23															
24															
25															
26															
27															
28															
29															
30															
31															

APRIL

NORTH LOUISIANA / ZONE 8

Start Indoors			Direct Sow			Plant Out Starts
basil	luffa	peppers, sweet	amaranth, grain	comfrey	mirliton/chayote	arrowroot
cucumbers	marjoram*	pumpkins	arugula	corn, sweet	okra	hops
cucuzza	Mexican tarragon	rosemary	asparagus crowns	daikon	peanuts	longevity spinach
cumin	mint	squash,	beans, bush	ginger	Southern peas	Okinawa spinach
cushaw	moringa*	summer	beans, climbing	honeydew	summer savory	Swiss chard
eggplant	New Zealand spinach	squash, winter	beans, winged	horseradish crowns	sunflower	tindora
fennel	oregano*	tomatillo	boniato slips	jicama	taro	
French tarragon	peppers, chili	tomatoes	borage	lovage	turmeric	
lemon balm		watermelon	cantaloupe	malanga	yacon tubers	
			carrots		yam tubers	

SOUTH LOUISIANA / ZONE 9

Start Indoors			Direct Sow			Plant Out Starts
basil	marjoram*	pumpkins	amaranth, grain	daikon	papalo/quilquina	arrowroot
cucumbers	Mexican tarragon	rosemary	asparagus crowns	ginger	peanuts	bay laurel
cucuzza	mint	squash, summer	beans, bush	honeydew	Southern peas	chaya
cumin	moringa*	squash, winter	beans, winged	jicama	summer savory	hops
cushaw	New Zealand spinach	tomatillo	boniato slips	lovage	sweet potato slips	katuk
eggplant	oregano*	tomatoes	cantaloupe	Malabar spinach	taro	longevity spinach
lemon balm	peppers, chili	watermelon	cassava	malanga	turmeric	Okinawa spinach
luffa	peppers, sweet		comfrey	molokhia	yacon tubers	Swiss chard
			corn, sweet	okra	yam tubers	tindora

FLOWERING POLLINATOR PLANTS FOR APRIL

Sow Seeds or Plant Starts

North Louisiana / Zone 8		Central Louisiana / Zone 9	
African daisies	gerberas daisies	African daisies	gomphrena
asters	lavender	asters	impatiens
cornflower	lobelia	bee balm	marigolds
bee balm	marigolds	Bulbine	nasturtiums
Bulbine	melampodium	celosia	nicotiana
calendula	nasturtiums	cleome	pentas
canna bulbs	nicotiana	coleus	phlox
cleome	nigella	coreopsis	rudbeckia
coreopsis	phlox	cosmos	salvias
cosmos	salvias	daylily bulbs	tithonia
crossandra	sunflowers	gaillardia	vinca
daylily bulbs	tithonia	gazania	zinnias
gaillardia	zinnias	gerbera daisies	
gazania			

Monthly Garden Tip:

Take advantage of early April's mild weather to plant quick-growing cool-season vegetables such as leaf lettuce, arugula, bok choy, tatsoi, radish, and even turnips.

Planting in containers allows gardeners to move delicate plants into shady spots during the afternoon heat. Shade cloth helps to ensure cooler temperatures in permanent in-ground or raised beds until the final harvest.

April 2023

Sunday	Monday	Tuesday	Wednesday	Thursday	Friday	Saturday
26	27	28	29	30	31	1
2	3	4	5	6	7	8
9	10	11	12	13	14	15
16	17	18	19	20	21	22
23	24	25	26	27	28	29
30	1	2	3	4	5	6

April

Week 14   04/03/23 - 04/09/23

○ 3. MONDAY

Garden Jobs for the Week

○ 4. TUESDAY

○ 5. WEDNESDAY

To Sow / Plant / Propagate

○ 6. THURSDAY

○ 7. FRIDAY

○ 8. SATURDAY / 9. SUNDAY

April

○ 10. MONDAY

Garden Jobs for the Week

○ 11. TUESDAY

○ 12. WEDNESDAY

To Sow / Plant / Propagate

○ 13. THURSDAY

○ 14. FRIDAY

○ 15. SATURDAY / 16. SUNDAY

April

Week 16   04/17/23 - 04/23/23

○ 17. MONDAY

Garden Jobs for the Week

_____

_____

○ 18. TUESDAY

_____

_____

_____

_____

_____

○ 19. WEDNESDAY

To Sow / Plant / Propagate

_____

_____

○ 20. THURSDAY

_____

_____

_____

_____

○ 21. FRIDAY

_____

_____

_____

_____

_____

○ 22. SATURDAY / 23. SUNDAY

_____

_____

_____

_____

April

Week 17   04/24/23 - 04/30/23

○ 24. MONDAY

Garden Jobs for the Week

_____

_____

○ 25. TUESDAY   _____

_____

_____

_____

_____

○ 26. WEDNESDAY

To Sow / Plant / Propagate

_____

_____

○ 27. THURSDAY   _____

_____

_____

_____

○ 28. FRIDAY   _____

_____

_____

_____

_____

○ 29. SATURDAY / 30. SUNDAY   _____

_____

_____

_____

Harvest Tracker

Month _____

Year _____

Day														Total
1														
2														
3														
4														
5														
6														
7														
8														
9														
10														
11														
12														
13														
14														
15														
16														
17														
18														
19														
20														
21														
22														
23														
24														
25														
26														
27														
28														
29														
30														
31														

MAY

NORTH LOUISIANA / ZONE 8

Start Indoors		Direct Sow		Plant Out Starts
basil	oregano*	beans, bush	Malabar spinach	arrowroot
cucuzza	peppers, chili	beans, climbing	malanga	bay laurel
lemon balm	peppers, sweet	beans, winged	molokhia	cucumbers
luffa	pumpkins	boniato slips	okra	cushaw
marjoram*	rosemary	cantaloupe	peanuts	daikon
Mexican tarragon	squash, summer	chufa	Southern peas	eggplant
mint	tomatillo	comfrey	summer savory	longevity spinach
moringa*	tomatoes	corn, sweet	sweet potato slips	Okinawa spinach
New Zealand spinach	watermelon	honeydew	taro	squash, winter
		jicama	yacon tubers	tindora
		lovage	yam tubers	

SOUTH LOUISIANA / ZONE 9

Start Indoors		Direct Sow		Plant Out Starts
basil	oregano*	boniato slips	molokhia	arrowroot
cucuzza	peppers, chili	cantaloupe	moringa*	bay laurel
eggplant	peppers, sweet	cassava	okra	chaya
lemon balm	pumpkins	chufa	peanuts	cushaw
luffa	squash, summer	daikon	Southern peas	katuk
marjoram*	tomatillo	honeydew	sweet potato slips	longevity spinach
mint	watermelon	jicama	taro	Okinawa spinach
New Zealand spinach		lovage	yacon tubers	squash, winter
		Malabar spinach	yam tubers	tindora
		malanga		tomatoes
				watermelon

FLOWERING POLLINATOR PLANTS FOR MAY

Sow Seeds or Plant Starts

North Louisiana / Zone 8		Central Louisiana / Zone 9	
African daisies	gerberas daisies	African daisies	impatiens
Angelonia	gomphrena	asters	nasturtiums
asters	marigolds	bee balm	pentas
bee balm	nasturtiums	Bulbine	portulaca
Bulbine	pentas	celosia	rudbeckia
celosia	rudbeckia	coleus	salvias
cleome	salvias	coreopsis	tithonia
coleus	tithonia	cosmos	torenia
coreopsis	vinca	gazania	vinca
daylily bulbs	zinnias	gerbera daisies	zinnias
gaillardia		gomphrena	
gazania			

Monthly Garden Tip:

May in the Gulf Coast states quickly becomes too hot and humid to plant any but the most heat-tolerant vegetables and fruits.

Consider adding varieties of your favorite edibles that have tropical origins, such as Southeast Asia, the Caribbean, and Central America. You'll be pleasantly surprised at how much they produce and how easily they fit into your menu.

Best of all, many varieties are perennial, and they'll provide years of delicious food with less work.

May 2023

Sunday	Monday	Tuesday	Wednesday	Thursday	Friday	Saturday
30	1	2	3	4	5	6
7	8	9	10	11	12	13
14	15	16	17	18	19	20
21	22	23	24	25	26	27
28	29	30	31	1	2	3

May

Week 18   05/01/23 - 05/07/23

○ 1. MONDAY

Garden Jobs for the Week

_____

_____

○ 2. TUESDAY

_____

_____

_____

_____

_____

○ 3. WEDNESDAY

To Sow / Plant / Propagate

_____

_____

○ 4. THURSDAY

_____

_____

_____

_____

○ 5. FRIDAY

_____

_____

_____

_____

○ 6. SATURDAY / 7. SUNDAY

_____

_____

_____

_____

May

Week 19   05/08/23 - 05/14/23

○ 8. MONDAY

Garden Jobs for the Week

_____
_____
_____
_____

○ 9. TUESDAY

_____
_____
_____
_____

○ 10. WEDNESDAY

To Sow / Plant / Propagate

_____
_____
_____

○ 11. THURSDAY

_____
_____
_____
_____

○ 12. FRIDAY

_____
_____
_____
_____

○ 13. SATURDAY / 14. SUNDAY

_____
_____
_____
_____

May

○ 15. MONDAY

Garden Jobs for the Week

_____

_____

_____

○ 16. TUESDAY

_____

_____

_____

_____

○ 17. WEDNESDAY

To Sow / Plant / Propagate

_____

_____

○ 18. THURSDAY

_____

_____

_____

_____

○ 19. FRIDAY

_____

_____

_____

_____

○ 20. SATURDAY / 21. SUNDAY

_____

_____

_____

_____

May

Week 21   05/22/23 - 05/28/23

○ 22. MONDAY

Garden Jobs for the Week

_____

_____

_____

○ 23. TUESDAY

_____

_____

_____

_____

○ 24. WEDNESDAY

To Sow / Plant / Propagate

_____

_____

○ 25. THURSDAY

_____

_____

_____

_____

_____

○ 26. FRIDAY

_____

_____

_____

_____

_____

○ 27. SATURDAY / 28. SUNDAY

_____

_____

_____

May

○ 29. MONDAY

Garden Jobs for the Week

○ 30. TUESDAY

○ 31. WEDNESDAY

To Sow / Plant / Propagate

○ 1. THURSDAY

○ 2. FRIDAY

○ 3. SATURDAY / 4. SUNDAY

Harvest Tracker

Month _____

Year _____

Day														Total
1														
2														
3														
4														
5														
6														
7														
8														
9														
10														
11														
12														
13														
14														
15														
16														
17														
18														
19														
20														
21														
22														
23														
24														
25														
26														
27														
28														
29														
30														
31														

JUNE
NORTH LOUISIANA / ZONE 8

Start Indoors		Direct Sow		Plant Out Starts
artichokes, globe*	pumpkins	boniato slips	molokhia	arrowroot
basil	sage*	cantaloupe	okra	bay laurel
cucuzza	squash, summer	chufa	peanuts	longevity spinach
eggplant	thyme*	daikon	Southern peas	Okinawa spinach
New Zealand spinach	tomatoes	honeydew	sweet potato slips	peppers, chili
peppers, sweet		Malabar spinach		tomatillo

SOUTH LOUISIANA / ZONE 9

Start Indoors		Direct Sow		Plant Out Starts
artichokes, globe*	peppers, sweet	boniato slips	molokhia	bay laurel
basil	pumpkins	cantaloupe	okra	longevity spinach
eggplant	tomatillo	cassava	peanuts	Okinawa spinach
moringa*	watermelon	chufa	Southern peas	peppers, chili
New Zealand spinach		cucuzza	squash, summer	
		daikon	sweet potato slips	
		honeydew	yam tubers	
		Malabar spinach		

FLOWERING POLLINATOR PLANTS FOR JUNE

Sow Seeds or Plant Starts

North Louisiana / Zone 8		South Louisiana / Zone 9	
asters	nasturtiums	asters	nasturtiums
bee balm	pentas	Bulbine	pentas
Bulbine	portulaca	celosia	portulaca
celosia	rudbeckia	coleus	salvias
coleus	salvias	coreopsis	vinca
gomphrena	vinca	gomphrena	
impatiens	zinnias	kalanchoe	
kalanchoe			
marigolds			

Monthly Garden Tip:

Heavy rains and swarms of insects make summer gardening in the South nearly impossible. Pests and disease are at a peak in June. That makes it an excellent month to sow summer cover crops. Cover crops help to prevent soil erosion from heavy rainstorms while protecting beneficial soil microorganisms from the blazing sun.

Good choices include velvet beans, hairy indigo, and soybeans. Once your cover crops flower, and before they set seed, cut the plants to the ground, and allow the foliage to decompose in place to add organic matter to the soil.

You can also plant cover crops to protect the soil while still ensuring a yield. Consider sweet potatoes and cow peas. Both will easily withstand the heat and humidity while improving the soil and providing a delicious harvest. Cow peas mature in about three months, just in time for harvesting before planting your fall garden. Sweet potatoes will deliver in four to five months' time, just in time for Thanksgiving.

June 2023

Sunday	Monday	Tuesday	Wednesday	Thursday	Friday	Saturday
28	29	30	31	1	2	3
4	5	6	7	8	9	10
11	12	13	14	15	16	17
18	19	20	21	22	23	24
25	26	27	28	29	30	1

June

Week 23   06/05/23 - 06/11/23

○ 5. MONDAY

Garden Jobs for the Week

○ 6. TUESDAY

○ 7. WEDNESDAY

To Sow / Plant / Propagate

○ 8. THURSDAY

○ 9. FRIDAY

○ 10. SATURDAY / 11. SUNDAY

June

Week 24   06/12/23 - 06/18/23

○ 12. MONDAY

Garden Jobs for the Week

_____

_____

_____

○ 13. TUESDAY

_____

_____

_____

_____

○ 14. WEDNESDAY

To Sow / Plant / Propagate

_____

_____

○ 15. THURSDAY

_____

_____

_____

_____

○ 16. FRIDAY

_____

_____

_____

_____

○ 17. SATURDAY / 18. SUNDAY

_____

_____

_____

_____

June

Week 25   06/19/23 - 06/25/23

○ 19. MONDAY

Garden Jobs for the Week

_____

_____

○ 20. TUESDAY

_____

_____

_____

_____

_____

○ 21. WEDNESDAY

To Sow / Plant / Propagate

_____

_____

○ 22. THURSDAY

_____

_____

_____

_____

_____

○ 23. FRIDAY

_____

_____

_____

_____

○ 24. SATURDAY / 25. SUNDAY

_____

_____

_____

_____

June

Week 26   06/26/23 - 07/02/23

○ 26. MONDAY

Garden Jobs for the Week

_____
_____
_____

○ 27. TUESDAY

_____
_____
_____
_____

○ 28. WEDNESDAY

To Sow / Plant / Propagate

_____
_____

○ 29. THURSDAY

_____
_____
_____
_____
_____

○ 30. FRIDAY

_____
_____
_____
_____

○ 1. SATURDAY / 2. SUNDAY

_____
_____
_____

Harvest Tracker

Month _____

Year _____

Day														Total
1														
2														
3														
4														
5														
6														
7														
8														
9														
10														
11														
12														
13														
14														
15														
16														
17														
18														
19														
20														
21														
22														
23														
24														
25														
26														
27														
28														
29														
30														
31														

JULY

NORTH LOUISIANA / ZONE 8

Start Indoors			Direct Sow		Plant Out Starts
artichokes, globe*	cucuzza	squash, summer	boniato slips	molokhia	longevity spinach
bok choy	eggplant	Swiss chard	cantaloupe	okra	New Zealand spinach
broccoli	kale	tatsoi	cassava	rutabaga	Okinawa spinach
cabbage	kohlrabi	thyme*	collards	Southern peas	peppers, sweet
cauliflower	moringa*	tomatoes	daikon	sunflower	tomatillo
Chinese cabbage	pumpkins		honeydew	sweet potato slips	watermelon
cucumbers	sage*		Irish potatoes	turnips	
			Malabar spinach		

SOUTH LOUISIANA / ZONE 9

Start Indoors		Direct Sow	Plant Out Starts
artichokes, globe*	New Zealand spinach	boniato slips	longevity spinach
basil	peppers, sweet	cantaloupe	Okinawa spinach
bok choy	pumpkins	daikon	
cauliflower	sage*	honeydew	
Chinese cabbage	squash, summer	Irish potatoes	
cucuzza	tatsoi	okra	
eggplant	thyme*	Southern peas	
kale	tomatoes	sunflower	
		sweet potato slips	

FLOWERING POLLINATOR PLANTS FOR JULY

Sow Seeds or Plant Starts

North Louisiana / Zone 8		South Louisiana / Zone 9	
asters	impatiens	asters	kalanchoe
bee balm	kalanchoe	Bulbine	nasturtiums
Bulbine	nasturtiums	celosia	pentas
butterfly lily	pentas	coleus	salvias
celosia	salvias	coreopsis	torenia
coleus	society garlic	Gladioli bulbs	
gaillardia	vinca	gomphrena	
gladioli bulbs	zinnias		
gomphrena			

Monthly Garden Tip:

Louisiana gardeners can get a head start on fall planting by starting many of their long-season vegetable plants indoors in late July. Tomatoes, eggplant, and peppers can all be grown in containers for several months until the conditions are right for planting out. Start them in large cell trays or soil blocks and then plant up into larger containers as needed. Once temperatures cool in September, you'll have large, healthy starter plants to add to the garden.

Prepare for coming gardening seasons by setting up a compost bin to capture the copious grass clippings that summer lawns provide. Mix fresh and dried clippings equally throughout the year, as well as any fallen leaves or other yard waste. Keep your compost pile moist and turn regularly, and you should have a rich, nutrient-filled soil amendment ready for the following spring gardening season.

July 2023

Sunday	Monday	Tuesday	Wednesday	Thursday	Friday	Saturday
25	26	27	28	29	30	1
2	3	4	5	6	7	8
9	10	11	12	13	14	15
16	17	18	19	20	21	22
23	24	25	26	27	28	29
30	31	1	2	3	4	5

July

07/03/23 - 07/09/23

○ 3. MONDAY

Garden Jobs for the Week

_____

_____

_____

○ 4. TUESDAY

_____

_____

_____

_____

_____

○ 5. WEDNESDAY

To Sow / Plant / Propagate

_____

_____

○ 6. THURSDAY

_____

_____

_____

_____

_____

○ 7. FRIDAY

_____

_____

_____

_____

_____

○ 8. SATURDAY / 9. SUNDAY

_____

_____

_____

_____

July

Week 28

○ 10. MONDAY

Garden Jobs for the Week

_____
_____
_____

○ 11. TUESDAY

_____
_____
_____
_____
_____

○ 12. WEDNESDAY

To Sow / Plant / Propagate

_____
_____
_____

○ 13. THURSDAY

_____
_____
_____
_____

○ 14. FRIDAY

_____
_____
_____
_____
_____

○ 15. SATURDAY / 16. SUNDAY

_____
_____
_____
_____

July

○ 17. MONDAY

Garden Jobs for the Week

○ 18. TUESDAY

○ 19. WEDNESDAY

To Sow / Plant / Propagate

○ 20. THURSDAY

○ 21. FRIDAY

○ 22. SATURDAY / 23. SUNDAY

July

Week 30   07/24/23 - 07/30/23

○ 24. MONDAY

Garden Jobs for the Week

○ 25. TUESDAY

○ 26. WEDNESDAY

To Sow / Plant / Propagate

○ 27. THURSDAY

○ 28. FRIDAY

○ 29. SATURDAY / 30. SUNDAY

July

Week 31   07/31/23 - 08/06/23

○ 31. MONDAY

Garden Jobs for the Week

○ 1. TUESDAY

○ 2. WEDNESDAY

To Sow / Plant / Propagate

○ 3. THURSDAY

○ 4. FRIDAY

○ 5. SATURDAY / 6. SUNDAY

Harvest Tracker

Month _____

Year _____

Day														Total
1														
2														
3														
4														
5														
6														
7														
8														
9														
10														
11														
12														
13														
14														
15														
16														
17														
18														
19														
20														
21														
22														
23														
24														
25														
26														
27														
28														
29														
30														
31														

AUGUST

NORTH LOUISIANA / ZONE 8

Start Indoors		Direct Sow		Plant Out Starts
bok choy	pumpkins	arugula	mustard	basil
broccoli	sage*	beets	radish	cucumbers
Brussels sprouts	Swiss chard	carrots	rutabaga	cucuzza
cabbage	tatsoi	collards	shallots	eggplant
cauliflower	thyme*	comfrey	sugarcane	kohlrabi
Chinese cabbage		Irish potatoes	sunflower	New Zealand spinach
		kale	turnips	okra
				squash, summer
				tomatoes

SOUTH LOUISIANA / ZONE 9

Start Indoors		Direct Sow		Plant Out Starts
bok choy	pumpkins	beets	radish	basil
broccoli	sage*	collards	rutabaga	eggplant
Brussels sprouts	squash, summer	Irish potatoes	shallots	longevity spinach
cabbage	Swiss chard	kale	Southern peas	Okinawa spinach
cauliflower	tatsoi	mustard	sunflower	peppers, sweet
Chinese cabbage	thyme*	okra	turnips	
cucumbers	tomatoes			
cucuzza				

FLOWERING POLLINATOR PLANTS FOR AUGUST

Sow Seeds or Plant Starts

North Louisiana / Zone 8		South Louisiana / Zone 9	
asters	gomphrena	asters	gomphrena
bee balm	melampodium	bee balm	kalanchoe
blanket flower	nasturtiums	Bulbine	nasturtiums
Bulbine	sunflowers	celosia	pentas
calendula	sweet alyssum	coleus	salvias
coleus	vinca	coreopsis	vinca
daylily bulbs			
gaillardia			

Monthly Garden Tip:

August is a good time to start sowing cool-season vegetables for the coming fall gardening season. Sow seeds in cell trays or soil blocks and keep under cover to prevent heat fatigue and wash-out from heavy summer rains. You can also start them indoors, where temperatures are cooler. Provide diffused sunlight, a sunny window, or broad-spectrum grow light once the seeds germinate. You can pot them up to larger containers as they grow until the outdoor conditions are optimal for planting out.

August also provides an opportunity to prep your garden beds for the fall growing season. Cut back or pull any weeds and gently aerate the soil with a garden fork. Add compost, composted manure, alfalfa pellets, and/or granular organic fertilizer to your fallow garden beds. Then, cover the beds with mulch or landscape fabric to kill off any active weed seeds. Make sure to water your fallow beds when necessary to help beneficial soil microbiology thrive until it's time to plant your fall garden starter plants.

August 2023

Sunday	Monday	Tuesday	Wednesday	Thursday	Friday	Saturday
30	31	1	2	3	4	5
6	7	8	9	10	11	12
13	14	15	16	17	18	19
20	21	22	23	24	25	26
27	28	29	30	31	1	2

August

Week 32   08/07/23 - 08/13/23

○ 7. MONDAY

Garden Jobs for the Week

_____

_____

○ 8. TUESDAY

_____

_____

_____

_____

_____

○ 9. WEDNESDAY

To Sow / Plant / Propagate

_____

_____

○ 10. THURSDAY

_____

_____

_____

_____

_____

○ 11. FRIDAY

_____

_____

_____

_____

○ 12. SATURDAY / 13. SUNDAY

_____

_____

_____

_____

August

Week 33   08/14/23 - 08/20/23

○ 14. MONDAY

Garden Jobs for the Week

_____

_____

_____

○ 15. TUESDAY

_____

_____

_____

_____

○ 16. WEDNESDAY

To Sow / Plant / Propagate

_____

_____

○ 17. THURSDAY

_____

_____

_____

_____

○ 18. FRIDAY

_____

_____

_____

_____

○ 19. SATURDAY / 20. SUNDAY

_____

_____

_____

August

Week 34   08/21/23 - 08/27/23

○ 21. MONDAY

Garden Jobs for the Week

_____

_____

_____

○ 22. TUESDAY

_____

_____

_____

_____

○ 23. WEDNESDAY

To Sow / Plant / Propagate

_____

_____

○ 24. THURSDAY

_____

_____

_____

_____

○ 25. FRIDAY

_____

_____

_____

_____

○ 26. SATURDAY / 27. SUNDAY

_____

_____

_____

August

Week 35   08/28/23 - 09/03/23

○ 28. MONDAY

Garden Jobs for the Week

_____

_____

○ 29. TUESDAY   _____

_____

_____

_____

_____

○ 30. WEDNESDAY

To Sow / Plant / Propagate

_____

○ 31. THURSDAY   _____

_____

_____

_____

_____

○ 1. FRIDAY   _____

_____

_____

_____

○ 2. SATURDAY / 3. SUNDAY   _____

_____

_____

_____

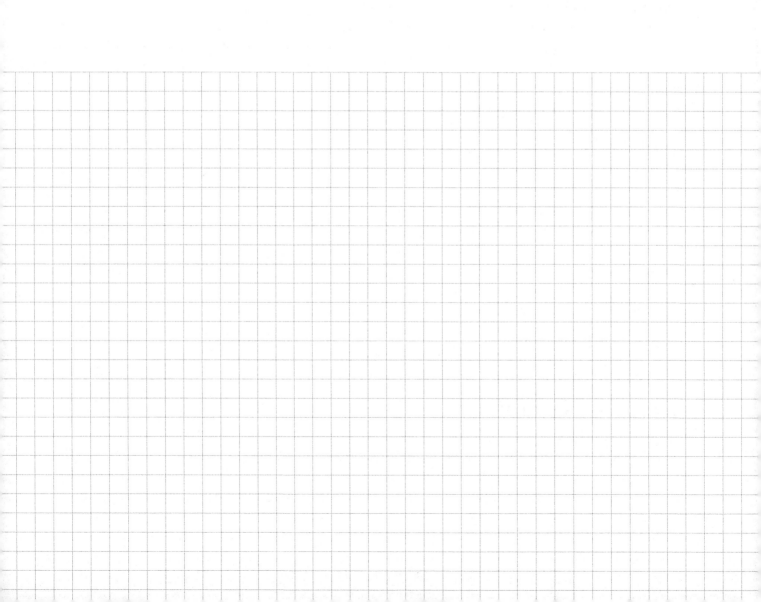

Harvest Tracker

Month _____

Year _____

Day														Total
1														
2														
3														
4														
5														
6														
7														
8														
9														
10														
11														
12														
13														
14														
15														
16														
17														
18														
19														
20														
21														
22														
23														
24														
25														
26														
27														
28														
29														
30														
31														

SEPTEMBER

NORTH LOUISIANA / ZONE 8

Start Indoors	Direct Sow		Plant Out Starts
bok choy	arugula	lettuce	artichokes, globe*
broccoli	beans, bush	mustard	kohlrabi
Brussels sprouts	beans, climbing	peas	pumpkins
cabbage	beets	radish	sage*
cauliflower	carrots	rutabaga	strawberry plants
Chinese cabbage	collards	shallots	thyme*
chives*	comfrey	spinach	
Swiss chard	garlic	sugarcane	
tatsoi	kale	turnips	

CENTRAL LOUISIANA / ZONE 9

Start Indoors		Direct Sow		Plant Out Starts
arugula	Chinese cabbage	beans, bush	mustard	artichokes, globe*
bok choy	chives*	beets	peas	pumpkins
broccoli	kohlrabi	carrots	radish	sage*
Brussels sprouts	spinach	comfrey	rutabaga	squash, summer
cabbage	Swiss chard	garlic	shallots	thyme*
cauliflower	tatsoi	Irish potatoes	sugarcane	
		kale	turnips	
		lettuce		

FLOWERING POLLINATOR PLANTS FOR SEPTEMBER

Sow Seeds or Plant Starts

North Louisiana / Zone 8		South Louisiana / Zone 9		
ageratum	gomphrena	ageratum	coreopsis	marigolds
asters	lavender	asters	cosmos	melampodium
cornflower	melampodium	cornflower	daylily bulbs	nasturtiums
bee balm	nigella	bee balm	gazania	nigella
calendula	nasturtiums	Bulbine	gerbera daisies	phlox
California poppy	petunias	gaillardia	gomphrena	sunflowers
celosia	phlox	salvias	impatiens	sweet alyssum
coleus	sunflowers	calendula	kalanchoe	vinca
daylily bulbs	zinnia	celosia	lobelia	zinnia
delphinium		coleus		

Monthly Garden Tip:

Sow pollinator-friendly annual flowers alongside your fall vegetables to attract beneficial insects, repel pest insects, and improve your garden soil. Some good choice for fall flower gardens in Louisiana are borage, chamomile, petunias, nasturtiums, and marigolds. Marigolds help repel root-knot nematodes and nasturtiums are an effective trap crop for aphids. Sunflowers will attract aphids and shield bugs, so plant them in a group about 6 to 10 feet from your garden beds to deter and trap these pests.

September 2023

Sunday	Monday	Tuesday	Wednesday	Thursday	Friday	Saturday
27	28	29	30	31	1	2
3	4	5	6	7	8	9
10	11	12	13	14	15	16
17	18	19	20	21	22	23
24	25	26	27	28	29	30

September

Week 36   09/04/23 - 09/10/23

○ 4. MONDAY

Garden Jobs for the Week

_____

_____

○ 5. TUESDAY

_____

_____

_____

_____

_____

○ 6. WEDNESDAY

To Sow / Plant / Propagate

_____

_____

○ 7. THURSDAY

_____

_____

_____

_____

_____

○ 8. FRIDAY

_____

_____

_____

_____

_____

○ 9. SATURDAY / 10. SUNDAY

_____

_____

_____

_____

September

Week 37   09/11/23 - 09/17/23

○ 11. MONDAY

Garden Jobs for the Week

_____

_____

_____

○ 12. TUESDAY

_____

_____

_____

_____

○ 13. WEDNESDAY

To Sow / Plant / Propagate

_____

_____

○ 14. THURSDAY

_____

_____

_____

_____

○ 15. FRIDAY

_____

_____

_____

_____

○ 16. SATURDAY / 17. SUNDAY

_____

_____

_____

_____

September

○ 18. MONDAY

Garden Jobs for the Week

○ 19. TUESDAY

○ 20. WEDNESDAY

To Sow / Plant / Propagate

○ 21. THURSDAY

○ 22. FRIDAY

○ 23. SATURDAY / 24. SUNDAY

September

Week 39   09/25/23 - 10/01/23

○ 25. MONDAY

Garden Jobs for the Week

_____

_____

_____

○ 26. TUESDAY

_____

_____

_____

_____

○ 27. WEDNESDAY

To Sow / Plant / Propagate

_____

_____

○ 28. THURSDAY

_____

_____

_____

_____

○ 29. FRIDAY

_____

_____

_____

_____

_____

○ 30. SATURDAY / 1. SUNDAY

_____

_____

_____

_____

Harvest Tracker

Month _____

Year _____

Day															Total
1															
2															
3															
4															
5															
6															
7															
8															
9															
10															
11															
12															
13															
14															
15															
16															
17															
18															
19															
20															
21															
22															
23															
24															
25															
26															
27															
28															
29															
30															
31															

OCTOBER

NORTH LOUISIANA / ZONE 8

Start Indoors	Direct Sow			Plant Out Starts
broccoli	beans, fava	garlic	salsify	bok choy
cabbage	beets	kale	shallots	Brussels sprouts
chives*	carrots	lettuce	spinach	cauliflower
cilantro	collards	mustard	sugarcane	Chinese cabbage
mitsuba	comfrey	parsnips	turnips	kohlrabi
parsley	dill	radish		strawberry plants
	endive	rutabaga		tatsoi

SOUTH LOUISIANA / ZONE 9

Start Indoors	Direct Sow			Plant Out Starts	
broccoli	arugula	comfrey	radish	bok choy	strawberry plants
cabbage	beans, bush	dill	rutabaga	Brussels sprouts	tatsoi
chives*	beans, fava	garlic	shallots	cauliflower	thyme*
kohlrabi	beets	kale	spinach	Chinese cabbage	
Swiss chard	carrots	lettuce	sugarcane	sage*	
	collards	mustard	turnips		

FLOWERING POLLINATOR PLANTS FOR OCTOBER

Sow Seeds or Plant Starts

North Louisiana / Zone 8		South Louisiana / Zone 9		
asters	lavender	agapanthus	delphinium	pansies
cornflower	nigella	asters	dianthus	petunias
bee balm	pansies	cornflower	gazania	phlox
California poppy	petunias	bee balm	gerbera daisies	salvias
dahlia bulbs	Shasta daisies	calendula	impatiens	snapdragons
delphinium	snapdragons	California poppy	lobelia	sunflowers
foxglove	sweet alyssum	celosia	marigolds	sweet alyssum
		coleus	melampodium	vinca
		cosmos	nasturtiums	zinnias
		dahlia bulbs	nigella	

Monthly Garden Tip:

October heralds the true start of the fall gardening season in Louisiana and the chance to grow traditional favorites that don't tolerate the heat. Plant brassicas such as cauliflower, broccoli, and cabbage, which you can blanch and freeze to enjoy throughout the year.

However, October can still bring hurricanes and storms, and sunlight is more intense after the autumnal solstice, burning fragile leaves on young plants. To ensure a regular supply of these garden staples, sow a round of starter plants in trays or soil blocks every 3 to 4 weeks throughout the late fall and winter. That way, you'll have replacement plants in case of extreme weather or unseasonable hot spells.

October 2023

Sunday	Monday	Tuesday	Wednesday	Thursday	Friday	Saturday
1	2	3	4	5	6	7
8	9	10	11	12	13	14
15	16	17	18	19	20	21
22	23	24	25	26	27	28
29	30	31	1	2	3	4

October

Week 40   10/02/23 - 10/08/23

○ 2. MONDAY

Garden Jobs for the Week

_____

_____

_____

○ 3. TUESDAY

_____

_____

_____

_____

○ 4. WEDNESDAY

To Sow / Plant / Propagate

_____

_____

○ 5. THURSDAY

_____

_____

_____

_____

○ 6. FRIDAY

_____

_____

_____

_____

○ 7. SATURDAY / 8. SUNDAY

_____

_____

_____

_____

October

Week 41   10/09/23 - 10/15/23

○ 9. MONDAY

Garden Jobs for the Week

_____
_____
_____
○ 10. TUESDAY
_____
_____
_____
_____

○ 11. WEDNESDAY

To Sow / Plant / Propagate

_____
_____
_____
○ 12. THURSDAY
_____
_____
_____
_____
○ 13. FRIDAY
_____
_____
_____
_____
○ 14. SATURDAY / 15. SUNDAY
_____
_____
_____
_____

October

Week 42   10/16/23 - 10/22/23

○ 16. MONDAY

Garden Jobs for the Week

_____

_____

○ 17. TUESDAY

_____

_____

_____

_____

_____

○ 18. WEDNESDAY

To Sow / Plant / Propagate

_____

_____

○ 19. THURSDAY

_____

_____

_____

_____

_____

○ 20. FRIDAY

_____

_____

_____

_____

○ 21. SATURDAY / 22. SUNDAY

_____

_____

_____

_____

October

Week 43   10/23/23 - 10/29/23

○ 23. MONDAY

Garden Jobs for the Week

_____

_____

_____

○ 24. TUESDAY   _____

_____

_____

_____

○ 25. WEDNESDAY

To Sow / Plant / Propagate

_____

_____

_____

○ 26. THURSDAY   _____

_____

_____

_____

○ 27. FRIDAY   _____

_____

_____

_____

_____

○ 28. SATURDAY / 29. SUNDAY   _____

_____

_____

_____

October

Week 44   10/30/23 - 11/05/23

○ 30. MONDAY

Garden Jobs for the Week

_____

_____

○ 31. TUESDAY

_____

_____

_____

_____

○ 1. WEDNESDAY

To Sow / Plant / Propagate

_____

_____

○ 2. THURSDAY

_____

_____

_____

_____

○ 3. FRIDAY

_____

_____

_____

_____

_____

○ 4. SATURDAY / 5. SUNDAY

_____

_____

_____

Harvest Tracker

Month _____

Year _____

Day															Total
1															
2															
3															
4															
5															
6															
7															
8															
9															
10															
11															
12															
13															
14															
15															
16															
17															
18															
19															
20															
21															
22															
23															
24															
25															
26															
27															
28															
29															
30															
31															

NOVEMBER

NORTH LOUISIANA / ZONE 8

Start Indoors		Direct Sow			
broccoli	cilantro	beans, fava	dill	parsnips	shallots
cabbage	mitsuba	beets	endive	peas	spinach
chives*	parsley	cardoon	garlic	salsify	sunchokes

SOUTH LOUISIANA / ZONE 9

Start Indoors	Direct Sow				Plant Out Starts
broccoli	beans, fava	garlic	peas		strawberry plants
cabbage	beets	kale	salsify		
chives*	carrots	lettuce mustard	shallots		
cilantro	dill	parsnips	spinach		
mitsuba	endive		sugarcane		
parsley					

FLOWERING POLLINATOR PLANTS FOR NOVEMBER

Sow Seeds or Plant Starts

North Louisiana / Zone 8		Central Louisiana / Zone 9	
asters	pansies	African daisies	impatiens
bee balm	pansies	asters	marigolds
dianthus	snapdragons	bee balm	nasturtiums
nigella	violas	calendula	nigella
		California poppy	pansies
		celosia	petunias
		crinum lilies	salvias
		dahlias	snapdragons
		delphinium	sweet alyssum
		dianthus	viola

Monthly Garden Tip:

November signals the beginning of the dry season in Louisiana, so you'll need to water more frequently. You can still install drip lines or soaker hoses to your garden beds before your seedlings become too large if you're careful.

Late fall is also a good time to apply a balanced organic fertilizer to your garden beds, landscape ornamentals, and lawn. Apply a slow-release formula according to the manufacturer's directions. You can supplement heavy feeders with a liquid formula as needed, if you choose.

Remember that many of our favorite landscape ornamentals are acid-loving plants, and will require a fertilizer specifically formulated for them. Azaleas, hydrangea, camellias, magnolias, and gardenias are classic flowering bushes for Southern gardens, and will all benefit from plant food for acid-loving plants.

November 2023

Sunday	Monday	Tuesday	Wednesday	Thursday	Friday	Saturday
29	30	31	1	2	3	4
5	6	7	8	9	10	11
12	13	14	15	16	17	18
19	20	21	22	23	24	25
26	27	28	29	30	1	2

November

Week 45   11/06/23 - 11/12/23

○ 6. MONDAY

Garden Jobs for the Week

_____

_____

○ 7. TUESDAY

_____

_____

_____

_____

_____

○ 8. WEDNESDAY

To Sow / Plant / Propagate

_____

_____

○ 9. THURSDAY

_____

_____

_____

_____

○ 10. FRIDAY

_____

_____

_____

_____

_____

○ 11. SATURDAY / 12. SUNDAY

_____

_____

_____

_____

November

11/13/23 - 11/19/23

○ 13. MONDAY

Garden Jobs for the Week

_____
_____
_____
_____
○ 14. TUESDAY

_____
_____
_____

○ 15. WEDNESDAY

To Sow / Plant / Propagate

_____
_____
_____
○ 16. THURSDAY

_____
_____
_____
_____
_____

○ 17. FRIDAY

_____
_____
_____
_____

○ 18. SATURDAY / 19. SUNDAY

_____
_____
_____

November

○ 20. MONDAY

Garden Jobs for the Week

_____

_____

_____

○ 21. TUESDAY

_____

_____

_____

_____

○ 22. WEDNESDAY

To Sow / Plant / Propagate

_____

_____

○ 23. THURSDAY

_____

_____

_____

_____

○ 24. FRIDAY

_____

_____

_____

_____

○ 25. SATURDAY / 26. SUNDAY

_____

_____

_____

November

Week 48   11/27/23 - 12/03/23

○ 27. MONDAY

Garden Jobs for the Week

_____

_____

_____

○ 28. TUESDAY

_____

_____

_____

_____

○ 29. WEDNESDAY

To Sow / Plant / Propagate

_____

_____

○ 30. THURSDAY

_____

_____

_____

_____

_____

○ 1. FRIDAY

_____

_____

_____

_____

○ 2. SATURDAY / 3. SUNDAY

_____

_____

_____

Harvest Tracker

Month _____

Year _____

Day															Total
1															
2															
3															
4															
5															
6															
7															
8															
9															
10															
11															
12															
13															
14															
15															
16															
17															
18															
19															
20															
21															
22															
23															
24															
25															
26															
27															
28															
29															
30															
31															

December

North Louisiana / Zone 8

Direct Sow or Plant Out Starts					
arugula	cardoon	chives	garlic	mizuna	rutabaga
beets	carrots	cilantro	kale	mustard	spinach
broccoli	cauliflower	comfrey	kohlrabi	onion sets	Swiss chard
Brussels sprouts	celeriac/celery	dill	lovage	parsley	thyme
cabbage	Chinese cabbage	fennel	turnips	radish	turnips

South Louisiana / Zone 9

Direct Sow or Plant Out Starts					
angelica	carrots	dill	kohlrabi	peas	sugar cane
arugula	cauliflower	endive	lettuce	radish	Swiss chard
beets	celeriac/celery	fennel	lovage	rutabaga	tatsoi
bok choy	chicory	garlic	mizuna	sage	thyme
broccoli	Chinese cabbage	green onions	mustard	shallots	turnips
Brussels sprouts	chives	Irish potatoes	New Zealand spinach	spinach	
cabbage	cilantro	kale	onion sets		
cardoon	collards		parsley		

Flowering Pollinator Plants for December

Sow Seeds or Plant Starts

North Louisiana / Zone 8	Central Louisiana / Zone 9
asters	asters
bee balm	bee balm
dianthus	dianthus
lobelia	pansies
pansies	petunias
petunias	snapdragons
snapdragons	
sweet alyssum	
viola	

Monthly Garden Tip:

Crisp, cool December days are perfect for winter garden cleanup. Cut back any overhanging tree branches to allow more sunlight into the garden. Prune dormant fruit trees and ornamentals to maintain their shape and increase flower and fruit production.

Collect fallen leaves as well as spent plants and pruning waste. Shred or chip your yard waste and add them to your compost pile. These materials add important minerals and additional carbon to your compost.

Prepare for the spring gardening season by cleaning and sharpening your garden tools. Wash and sterilize pots and starter trays. Check your Annual Edible Plant logs to see which varieties performed best and order seeds for next year.

Make sure to order your copy of the 2024 Southern Garden Louisiana Gardening Planner to make garden planning easier and more successful.

December 2023

Sunday	Monday	Tuesday	Wednesday	Thursday	Friday	Saturday
26	27	28	29	30	1	2
3	4	5	6	7	8	9
10	11	12	13	14	15	16
17	18	19	20	21	22	23
24	25	26	27	28	29	30
31	1	2	3	4	5	6

December

○ 4. MONDAY

Garden Jobs for the Week

○ 5. TUESDAY

○ 6. WEDNESDAY

To Sow / Plant / Propagate

○ 7. THURSDAY

○ 8. FRIDAY

○ 9. SATURDAY / 10. SUNDAY

December

Week 50

○ 11. MONDAY

Garden Jobs for the Week

_____

_____

○ 12. TUESDAY

_____

_____

_____

_____

○ 13. WEDNESDAY

To Sow / Plant / Propagate

_____

_____

○ 14. THURSDAY

_____

_____

_____

_____

○ 15. FRIDAY

_____

_____

_____

_____

○ 16. SATURDAY / 17. SUNDAY

_____

_____

_____

December

Week 51   12/18/23 - 12/24/23

○ 18. MONDAY

Garden Jobs for the Week

_____

_____

_____

○ 19. TUESDAY

_____

_____

_____

_____

_____

○ 20. WEDNESDAY

To Sow / Plant / Propagate

_____

_____

○ 21. THURSDAY

_____

_____

_____

_____

_____

○ 22. FRIDAY

_____

_____

_____

_____

_____

○ 23. SATURDAY / 24. SUNDAY

_____

_____

_____

_____

December

Week 52

○ 25. MONDAY

Garden Jobs for the Week

_____
_____
_____
○ 26. TUESDAY
_____
_____
_____
_____

○ 27. WEDNESDAY

To Sow / Plant / Propagate

_____
_____
_____
○ 28. THURSDAY
_____
_____
_____
_____
_____
_____
○ 29. FRIDAY
_____
_____
_____
_____
_____
○ 30. SATURDAY / 31. SUNDAY
_____
_____
_____
_____

Logging Tools

Annual Edible Plant Log

Plant _____ Variety _____ Hybrid ☐ Heirloom ☐ Open-Pollinated ☐

Disease Resistance_____Seed ☐ Transplant ☐ Cutting ☐

Date Acquired:_____Source: _____

Germination Stage

Water Requirements:_____Light Requirements:_____Feeding Schedule:_____

Foliage Development Stage

Water Requirements:_____Light Requirements:_____Feeding Schedule:_____

Flowering

Water Requirements:_____Light Requirements:_____Feeding Schedule:_____

Fruiting

Water Requirements:_____Light Requirements:_____Feeding Schedule:_____

	Date	Notes & Observations		Date	Notes & Observations
Sown			Week 10:		
Planted			Week 11:		
Week 1:			Week 12:		
Week 2:			Week 13:		
Week 3:			Week 14:		
Week 4:			Week 15:		
Week 5:			Week 16:		
Week 6:			Week 17:		
Week 7:			Week 18:		
Week 8:			Week 19:		
Week 9:			Week 20:		
Harvest:					

Storage Notes: Fresh ☐ Canned ☐ Dried ☐ Frozen ☐ Freeze-dried ☐

Flavor/Texture: _____

Shelf Life _____

Observations _____

_____

_____

Annual Edible Plant Log

Plant _____ Variety _____ Hybrid ☐ Heirloom ☐ Open-Pollinated ☐

Disease Resistance_____Seed ☐ Transplant ☐ Cutting ☐

Date Acquired:_____Source: _____

Germination Stage

Water Requirements:_____Light Requirements:_____Feeding Schedule:_____

Foliage Development Stage

Water Requirements:_____Light Requirements:_____Feeding Schedule:_____

Flowering

Water Requirements:_____Light Requirements:_____Feeding Schedule:_____

Fruiting

Water Requirements:_____Light Requirements:_____Feeding Schedule:_____

	Date	Notes & Observations		Date	Notes & Observations
Sown			Week 10:		
Planted			Week 11:		
Week 1:			Week 12:		
Week 2:			Week 13:		
Week 3:			Week 14:		
Week 4:			Week 15:		
Week 5:			Week 16:		
Week 6:			Week 17:		
Week 7:			Week 18:		
Week 8:			Week 19:		
Week 9:			Week 20:		
Harvest:					

Storage Notes: Fresh ☐ Canned ☐ Dried ☐ Frozen ☐ Freeze-dried ☐

Flavor/Texture: _____

Shelf Life _____

Observations _____

_____

_____

Annual Edible Plant Log

Plant _____ Variety _____ Hybrid ☐ Heirloom ☐ Open-Pollinated ☐

Disease Resistance_____Seed ☐ Transplant ☐ Cutting ☐

Date Acquired:_____Source: _____

Germination Stage

Water Requirements:_____Light Requirements:_____Feeding Schedule:_____

Foliage Development Stage

Water Requirements:_____Light Requirements:_____Feeding Schedule:_____

Flowering

Water Requirements:_____Light Requirements:_____Feeding Schedule:_____

Fruiting

Water Requirements:_____Light Requirements:_____Feeding Schedule:_____

	Date	Notes & Observations		Date	Notes & Observations
Sown			Week 10:		
Planted			Week 11:		
Week 1:			Week 12:		
Week 2:			Week 13:		
Week 3:			Week 14:		
Week 4:			Week 15:		
Week 5:			Week 16:		
Week 6:			Week 17:		
Week 7:			Week 18:		
Week 8:			Week 19:		
Week 9:			Week 20:		
Harvest:					

Storage Notes: Fresh ☐   Canned ☐   Dried ☐   Frozen ☐   Freeze-dried ☐

Flavor/Texture: _____

Shelf Life   _____

Observations   _____

_____

_____

Annual Edible Plant Log

Plant _____ Variety _____ Hybrid ☐ Heirloom ☐ Open-Pollinated ☐

Disease Resistance _____ Seed ☐ Transplant ☐ Cutting ☐

Date Acquired: _____ Source: _____

Germination Stage

Water Requirements: _____ Light Requirements: _____ Feeding Schedule: _____

Foliage Development Stage

Water Requirements: _____ Light Requirements: _____ Feeding Schedule: _____

Flowering

Water Requirements: _____ Light Requirements: _____ Feeding Schedule: _____

Fruiting

Water Requirements: _____ Light Requirements: _____ Feeding Schedule: _____

	Date	Notes & Observations		Date	Notes & Observations
Sown			Week 10:		
Planted			Week 11:		
Week 1:			Week 12:		
Week 2:			Week 13:		
Week 3:			Week 14:		
Week 4:			Week 15:		
Week 5:			Week 16:		
Week 6:			Week 17:		
Week 7:			Week 18:		
Week 8:			Week 19:		
Week 9:			Week 20:		
Harvest:					

Storage Notes: Fresh ☐   Canned ☐   Dried ☐   Frozen ☐   Freeze-dried ☐

Flavor/Texture: _____

Shelf Life _____

Observations _____

_____

_____

Annual Edible Plant Log

Plant _____ Variety _____ Hybrid ☐ Heirloom ☐ Open-Pollinated ☐

Disease Resistance_____Seed ☐ Transplant ☐ Cutting ☐

Date Acquired:_____Source: _____

Germination Stage

Water Requirements:_____Light Requirements:_____Feeding Schedule:_____

Foliage Development Stage

Water Requirements:_____Light Requirements:_____Feeding Schedule:_____

Flowering

Water Requirements:_____Light Requirements:_____Feeding Schedule:_____

Fruiting

Water Requirements:_____Light Requirements:_____Feeding Schedule:_____

	Date	Notes & Observations		Date	Notes & Observations
Sown			Week 10:		
Planted			Week 11:		
Week 1:			Week 12:		
Week 2:			Week 13:		
Week 3:			Week 14:		
Week 4:			Week 15:		
Week 5:			Week 16:		
Week 6:			Week 17:		
Week 7:			Week 18:		
Week 8:			Week 19:		
Week 9:			Week 20:		
Harvest:					

Storage Notes: Fresh ☐   Canned ☐   Dried ☐   Frozen ☐   Freeze-dried ☐

Flavor/Texture: _____

Shelf Life _____

Observations _____

_____

_____

Annual Edible Plant Log

Plant _____ Variety _____ Hybrid ☐ Heirloom ☐ Open-Pollinated ☐

Disease Resistance_____Seed ☐ Transplant ☐ Cutting ☐

Date Acquired:_____Source: _____

Germination Stage

Water Requirements:_____Light Requirements:_____Feeding Schedule:_____

Foliage Development Stage

Water Requirements:_____Light Requirements:_____Feeding Schedule:_____

Flowering

Water Requirements:_____Light Requirements:_____Feeding Schedule:_____

Fruiting

Water Requirements:_____Light Requirements:_____Feeding Schedule:_____

	Date	Notes & Observations		Date	Notes & Observations
Sown			Week 10:		
Planted			Week 11:		
Week 1:			Week 12:		
Week 2:			Week 13:		
Week 3:			Week 14:		
Week 4:			Week 15:		
Week 5:			Week 16:		
Week 6:			Week 17:		
Week 7:			Week 18:		
Week 8:			Week 19:		
Week 9:			Week 20:		
Harvest:					

Storage Notes: Fresh ☐   Canned ☐   Dried ☐   Frozen ☐   Freeze-dried ☐

Flavor/Texture: _____

Shelf Life   _____

Observations   _____

_____

_____

Annual Edible Plant Log

Plant _____ Variety _____ Hybrid ☐ Heirloom ☐ Open-Pollinated ☐

Disease Resistance_____Seed ☐ Transplant ☐ Cutting ☐

Date Acquired:_____Source: _____

Germination Stage

Water Requirements:_____Light Requirements:_____Feeding Schedule:_____

Foliage Development Stage

Water Requirements:_____Light Requirements:_____Feeding Schedule:_____

Flowering

Water Requirements:_____Light Requirements:_____Feeding Schedule:_____

Fruiting

Water Requirements:_____Light Requirements:_____Feeding Schedule:_____

	Date	Notes & Observations		Date	Notes & Observations
Sown			Week 10:		
Planted			Week 11:		
Week 1:			Week 12:		
Week 2:			Week 13:		
Week 3:			Week 14:		
Week 4:			Week 15:		
Week 5:			Week 16:		
Week 6:			Week 17:		
Week 7:			Week 18:		
Week 8:			Week 19:		
Week 9:			Week 20:		
Harvest:					

Storage Notes: Fresh ☐   Canned ☐   Dried ☐   Frozen ☐   Freeze-dried ☐

Flavor/Texture: _____

Shelf Life   _____

Observations   _____

_____

_____

Annual Edible Plant Log

Plant _____ Variety _____ Hybrid ☐ Heirloom ☐ Open-Pollinated ☐

Disease Resistance_____Seed ☐ Transplant ☐ Cutting ☐

Date Acquired:_____Source: _____

Germination Stage

Water Requirements:_____Light Requirements:_____Feeding Schedule:_____

Foliage Development Stage

Water Requirements:_____Light Requirements:_____Feeding Schedule:_____

Flowering

Water Requirements:_____Light Requirements:_____Feeding Schedule:_____

Fruiting

Water Requirements:_____Light Requirements:_____Feeding Schedule:_____

	Date	Notes & Observations		Date	Notes & Observations
Sown			Week 10:		
Planted			Week 11:		
Week 1:			Week 12:		
Week 2:			Week 13:		
Week 3:			Week 14:		
Week 4:			Week 15:		
Week 5:			Week 16:		
Week 6:			Week 17:		
Week 7:			Week 18:		
Week 8:			Week 19:		
Week 9:			Week 20:		
Harvest:					

Storage Notes: Fresh ☐ Canned ☐ Dried ☐ Frozen ☐ Freeze-dried ☐

Flavor/Texture: _____

Shelf Life _____

Observations _____

_____

Annual Edible Plant Log

Plant _____ Variety _____ Hybrid ☐ Heirloom ☐ Open-Pollinated ☐

Disease Resistance_____Seed ☐ Transplant ☐ Cutting ☐

Date Acquired:_____Source: _____

Germination Stage

Water Requirements:_____Light Requirements:_____Feeding Schedule:_____

Foliage Development Stage

Water Requirements:_____Light Requirements:_____Feeding Schedule:_____

Flowering

Water Requirements:_____Light Requirements:_____Feeding Schedule:_____

Fruiting

Water Requirements:_____Light Requirements:_____Feeding Schedule:_____

	Date	Notes & Observations		Date	Notes & Observations
Sown			Week 10:		
Planted			Week 11:		
Week 1:			Week 12:		
Week 2:			Week 13:		
Week 3:			Week 14:		
Week 4:			Week 15:		
Week 5:			Week 16:		
Week 6:			Week 17:		
Week 7:			Week 18:		
Week 8:			Week 19:		
Week 9:			Week 20:		
Harvest:					

Storage Notes: Fresh ☐   Canned ☐   Dried ☐   Frozen ☐   Freeze-dried ☐

Flavor/Texture: _____

Shelf Life _____

Observations _____

_____

Annual Edible Plant Log

Plant _____ Variety _____ Hybrid ☐ Heirloom ☐ Open-Pollinated ☐

Disease Resistance_____Seed ☐ Transplant ☐ Cutting ☐

Date Acquired:_____Source: _____

Germination Stage

Water Requirements:_____Light Requirements:_____Feeding Schedule:_____

Foliage Development Stage

Water Requirements:_____Light Requirements:_____Feeding Schedule:_____

Flowering

Water Requirements:_____Light Requirements:_____Feeding Schedule:_____

Fruiting

Water Requirements:_____Light Requirements:_____Feeding Schedule:_____

	Date	Notes & Observations		Date	Notes & Observations
Sown			Week 10:		
Planted			Week 11:		
Week 1:			Week 12:		
Week 2:			Week 13:		
Week 3:			Week 14:		
Week 4:			Week 15:		
Week 5:			Week 16:		
Week 6:			Week 17:		
Week 7:			Week 18:		
Week 8:			Week 19:		
Week 9:			Week 20:		
Harvest:					

Storage Notes: Fresh ☐   Canned ☐   Dried ☐   Frozen ☐   Freeze-dried ☐

Flavor/Texture: _____

Shelf Life   _____

Observations   _____

_____

_____

Annual Edible Plant Log

Plant _____ Variety _____ Hybrid ☐ Heirloom ☐ Open-Pollinated ☐

Disease Resistance_____Seed ☐ Transplant ☐ Cutting ☐

Date Acquired:_____Source: _____

Germination Stage

Water Requirements:_____Light Requirements:_____Feeding Schedule:_____

Foliage Development Stage

Water Requirements:_____Light Requirements:_____Feeding Schedule:_____

Flowering

Water Requirements:_____Light Requirements:_____Feeding Schedule:_____

Fruiting

Water Requirements:_____Light Requirements:_____Feeding Schedule:_____

	Date	Notes & Observations		Date	Notes & Observations
Sown			Week 10:		
Planted			Week 11:		
Week 1:			Week 12:		
Week 2:			Week 13:		
Week 3:			Week 14:		
Week 4:			Week 15:		
Week 5:			Week 16:		
Week 6:			Week 17:		
Week 7:			Week 18:		
Week 8:			Week 19:		
Week 9:			Week 20:		
Harvest:					

Storage Notes: Fresh ☐   Canned ☐   Dried ☐   Frozen ☐   Freeze-dried ☐

Flavor/Texture: _____

Shelf Life _____

Observations _____

_____

_____

Annual Edible Plant Log

Plant _____ Variety _____ Hybrid ☐ Heirloom ☐ Open-Pollinated ☐

Disease Resistance_____Seed ☐ Transplant ☐ Cutting ☐

Date Acquired:_____Source: _____

Germination Stage

Water Requirements:_____Light Requirements:_____Feeding Schedule:_____

Foliage Development Stage

Water Requirements:_____Light Requirements:_____Feeding Schedule:_____

Flowering

Water Requirements:_____Light Requirements:_____Feeding Schedule:_____

Fruiting

Water Requirements:_____Light Requirements:_____Feeding Schedule:_____

	Date	Notes & Observations		Date	Notes & Observations
Sown			Week 10:		
Planted			Week 11:		
Week 1:			Week 12:		
Week 2:			Week 13:		
Week 3:			Week 14:		
Week 4:			Week 15:		
Week 5:			Week 16:		
Week 6:			Week 17:		
Week 7:			Week 18:		
Week 8:			Week 19:		
Week 9:			Week 20:		
Harvest:					

Storage Notes: Fresh ☐   Canned ☐   Dried ☐   Frozen ☐   Freeze-dried ☐

Flavor/Texture: _____

Shelf Life _____

Observations _____

_____

_____

Annual Edible Plant Log

Plant _____ Variety _____ Hybrid ☐ Heirloom ☐ Open-Pollinated ☐

Disease Resistance_____Seed ☐ Transplant ☐ Cutting ☐

Date Acquired:_____Source: _____

Germination Stage

Water Requirements:_____Light Requirements:_____Feeding Schedule:_____

Foliage Development Stage

Water Requirements:_____Light Requirements:_____Feeding Schedule:_____

Flowering

Water Requirements:_____Light Requirements:_____Feeding Schedule:_____

Fruiting

Water Requirements:_____Light Requirements:_____Feeding Schedule:_____

	Date	Notes & Observations		Date	Notes & Observations
Sown			Week 10:		
Planted			Week 11:		
Week 1:			Week 12:		
Week 2:			Week 13:		
Week 3:			Week 14:		
Week 4:			Week 15:		
Week 5:			Week 16:		
Week 6:			Week 17:		
Week 7:			Week 18:		
Week 8:			Week 19:		
Week 9:			Week 20:		
Harvest:					

Storage Notes: Fresh ☐   Canned ☐   Dried ☐   Frozen ☐   Freeze-dried ☐

Flavor/Texture: _____

Shelf Life   _____

Observations   _____

_____

_____

Annual Edible Plant Log

Plant _____ Variety _____ Hybrid ☐ Heirloom ☐ Open-Pollinated ☐

Disease Resistance_____Seed ☐ Transplant ☐ Cutting ☐

Date Acquired:_____Source: _____

Germination Stage

Water Requirements:_____Light Requirements:_____Feeding Schedule:_____

Foliage Development Stage

Water Requirements:_____Light Requirements:_____Feeding Schedule:_____

Flowering

Water Requirements:_____Light Requirements:_____Feeding Schedule:_____

Fruiting

Water Requirements:_____Light Requirements:_____Feeding Schedule:_____

	Date	Notes & Observations		Date	Notes & Observations
Sown			Week 10:		
Planted			Week 11:		
Week 1:			Week 12:		
Week 2:			Week 13:		
Week 3:			Week 14:		
Week 4:			Week 15:		
Week 5:			Week 16:		
Week 6:			Week 17:		
Week 7:			Week 18:		
Week 8:			Week 19:		
Week 9:			Week 20:		
Harvest:					

Storage Notes: Fresh ☐   Canned ☐   Dried ☐   Frozen ☐   Freeze-dried ☐

Flavor/Texture: _____

Shelf Life _____

Observations _____

_____

_____

Annual Edible Plant Log

Plant _____ Variety _____ Hybrid ☐ Heirloom ☐ Open-Pollinated ☐

Disease Resistance _____ Seed ☐ Transplant ☐ Cutting ☐

Date Acquired: _____ Source: _____

Germination Stage

Water Requirements: _____ Light Requirements: _____ Feeding Schedule: _____

Foliage Development Stage

Water Requirements: _____ Light Requirements: _____ Feeding Schedule: _____

Flowering

Water Requirements: _____ Light Requirements: _____ Feeding Schedule: _____

Fruiting

Water Requirements: _____ Light Requirements: _____ Feeding Schedule: _____

	Date	Notes & Observations		Date	Notes & Observations
Sown			Week 10:		
Planted			Week 11:		
Week 1:			Week 12:		
Week 2:			Week 13:		
Week 3:			Week 14:		
Week 4:			Week 15:		
Week 5:			Week 16:		
Week 6:			Week 17:		
Week 7:			Week 18:		
Week 8:			Week 19:		
Week 9:			Week 20:		
Harvest:					

Storage Notes: Fresh ☐ Canned ☐ Dried ☐ Frozen ☐ Freeze-dried ☐

Flavor/Texture: _____

Shelf Life _____

Observations _____

_____

_____

Annual Edible Plant Log

Plant _____ Variety _____ Hybrid ☐ Heirloom ☐ Open-Pollinated ☐

Disease Resistance _____ Seed ☐ Transplant ☐ Cutting ☐

Date Acquired: _____ Source: _____

Germination Stage

Water Requirements: _____ Light Requirements: _____ Feeding Schedule: _____

Foliage Development Stage

Water Requirements: _____ Light Requirements: _____ Feeding Schedule: _____

Flowering

Water Requirements: _____ Light Requirements: _____ Feeding Schedule: _____

Fruiting

Water Requirements: _____ Light Requirements: _____ Feeding Schedule: _____

	Date	Notes & Observations		Date	Notes & Observations
Sown			Week 10:		
Planted			Week 11:		
Week 1:			Week 12:		
Week 2:			Week 13:		
Week 3:			Week 14:		
Week 4:			Week 15:		
Week 5:			Week 16:		
Week 6:			Week 17:		
Week 7:			Week 18:		
Week 8:			Week 19:		
Week 9:			Week 20:		
Harvest:					

Storage Notes: Fresh ☐ Canned ☐ Dried ☐ Frozen ☐ Freeze-dried ☐

Flavor/Texture: _____

Shelf Life _____

Observations _____

_____

_____

Annual Edible Plant Log

Plant _____ Variety _____ Hybrid ☐ Heirloom ☐ Open-Pollinated ☐

Disease Resistance_____Seed ☐ Transplant ☐ Cutting ☐

Date Acquired:_____Source: _____

Germination Stage

Water Requirements:_____Light Requirements:_____Feeding Schedule:_____

Foliage Development Stage

Water Requirements:_____Light Requirements:_____Feeding Schedule:_____

Flowering

Water Requirements:_____Light Requirements:_____Feeding Schedule:_____

Fruiting

Water Requirements:_____Light Requirements:_____Feeding Schedule:_____

	Date	Notes & Observations		Date	Notes & Observations
Sown			Week 10:		
Planted			Week 11:		
Week 1:			Week 12:		
Week 2:			Week 13:		
Week 3:			Week 14:		
Week 4:			Week 15:		
Week 5:			Week 16:		
Week 6:			Week 17:		
Week 7:			Week 18:		
Week 8:			Week 19:		
Week 9:			Week 20:		
Harvest:					

Storage Notes: Fresh ☐   Canned ☐   Dried ☐   Frozen ☐   Freeze-dried ☐

Flavor/Texture: _____

Shelf Life   _____

Observations   _____

_____

_____

Annual Edible Plant Log

Plant _____ Variety _____ Hybrid ☐ Heirloom ☐ Open-Pollinated ☐

Disease Resistance_____Seed ☐ Transplant ☐ Cutting ☐

Date Acquired:_____Source: _____

Germination Stage

Water Requirements:_____Light Requirements:_____Feeding Schedule:_____

Foliage Development Stage

Water Requirements:_____Light Requirements:_____Feeding Schedule:_____

Flowering

Water Requirements:_____Light Requirements:_____Feeding Schedule:_____

Fruiting

Water Requirements:_____Light Requirements:_____Feeding Schedule:_____

	Date	Notes & Observations		Date	Notes & Observations
Sown			Week 10:		
Planted			Week 11:		
Week 1:			Week 12:		
Week 2:			Week 13:		
Week 3:			Week 14:		
Week 4:			Week 15:		
Week 5:			Week 16:		
Week 6:			Week 17:		
Week 7:			Week 18:		
Week 8:			Week 19:		
Week 9:			Week 20:		
Harvest:					

Storage Notes: Fresh ☐   Canned ☐   Dried ☐   Frozen ☐   Freeze-dried ☐

Flavor/Texture: _____

Shelf Life _____

Observations _____

_____

_____

Annual Edible Plant Log

Plant _____ Variety _____ Hybrid ☐ Heirloom ☐ Open-Pollinated ☐

Disease Resistance _____ Seed ☐ Transplant ☐ Cutting ☐

Date Acquired: _____ Source: _____

Germination Stage

Water Requirements: _____ Light Requirements: _____ Feeding Schedule: _____

Foliage Development Stage

Water Requirements: _____ Light Requirements: _____ Feeding Schedule: _____

Flowering

Water Requirements: _____ Light Requirements: _____ Feeding Schedule: _____

Fruiting

Water Requirements: _____ Light Requirements: _____ Feeding Schedule: _____

	Date	Notes & Observations		Date	Notes & Observations
Sown			Week 10:		
Planted			Week 11:		
Week 1:			Week 12:		
Week 2:			Week 13:		
Week 3:			Week 14:		
Week 4:			Week 15:		
Week 5:			Week 16:		
Week 6:			Week 17:		
Week 7:			Week 18:		
Week 8:			Week 19:		
Week 9:			Week 20:		
Harvest:					

Storage Notes: Fresh ☐   Canned ☐   Dried ☐   Frozen ☐   Freeze-dried ☐

Flavor/Texture: _____

Shelf Life _____

Observations _____

_____

_____

Annual Edible Plant Log

Plant _____ Variety _____ Hybrid ☐ Heirloom ☐ Open-Pollinated ☐

Disease Resistance_____Seed ☐ Transplant ☐ Cutting ☐

Date Acquired:_____Source: _____

Germination Stage

Water Requirements:_____Light Requirements:_____Feeding Schedule:_____

Foliage Development Stage

Water Requirements:_____Light Requirements:_____Feeding Schedule:_____

Flowering

Water Requirements:_____Light Requirements:_____Feeding Schedule:_____

Fruiting

Water Requirements:_____Light Requirements:_____Feeding Schedule:_____

	Date	Notes & Observations		Date	Notes & Observations
Sown			Week 10:		
Planted			Week 11:		
Week 1:			Week 12:		
Week 2:			Week 13:		
Week 3:			Week 14:		
Week 4:			Week 15:		
Week 5:			Week 16:		
Week 6:			Week 17:		
Week 7:			Week 18:		
Week 8:			Week 19:		
Week 9:			Week 20:		
Harvest:					

Storage Notes: Fresh ☐   Canned ☐   Dried ☐   Frozen ☐   Freeze-dried ☐

Flavor/Texture: _____

Shelf Life _____

Observations _____

_____

_____

Annual Edible Plant Log

Plant _____ Variety _____ Hybrid ☐ Heirloom ☐ Open-Pollinated ☐

Disease Resistance_____Seed ☐ Transplant ☐ Cutting ☐

Date Acquired:_____Source: _____

Germination Stage

Water Requirements:_____Light Requirements:_____Feeding Schedule:_____

Foliage Development Stage

Water Requirements:_____Light Requirements:_____Feeding Schedule:_____

Flowering

Water Requirements:_____Light Requirements:_____Feeding Schedule:_____

Fruiting

Water Requirements:_____Light Requirements:_____Feeding Schedule:_____

	Date	Notes & Observations		Date	Notes & Observations
Sown			Week 10:		
Planted			Week 11:		
Week 1:			Week 12:		
Week 2:			Week 13:		
Week 3:			Week 14:		
Week 4:			Week 15:		
Week 5:			Week 16:		
Week 6:			Week 17:		
Week 7:			Week 18:		
Week 8:			Week 19:		
Week 9:			Week 20:		
Harvest:					

Storage Notes: Fresh ☐   Canned ☐   Dried ☐   Frozen ☐   Freeze-dried ☐

Flavor/Texture: _____

Shelf Life _____

Observations _____

_____

_____

Annual Edible Plant Log

Plant _____ Variety _____ Hybrid ☐ Heirloom ☐ Open-Pollinated ☐

Disease Resistance_____Seed ☐ Transplant ☐ Cutting ☐

Date Acquired:_____ Source: _____

Germination Stage

Water Requirements:_____Light Requirements:_____Feeding Schedule:_____

Foliage Development Stage

Water Requirements:_____Light Requirements:_____Feeding Schedule:_____

Flowering

Water Requirements:_____Light Requirements:_____Feeding Schedule:_____

Fruiting

Water Requirements:_____Light Requirements:_____Feeding Schedule:_____

	Date	Notes & Observations		Date	Notes & Observations
Sown			Week 10:		
Planted			Week 11:		
Week 1:			Week 12:		
Week 2:			Week 13:		
Week 3:			Week 14:		
Week 4:			Week 15:		
Week 5:			Week 16:		
Week 6:			Week 17:		
Week 7:			Week 18:		
Week 8:			Week 19:		
Week 9:			Week 20:		
Harvest:					

Storage Notes: Fresh ☐   Canned ☐   Dried ☐   Frozen ☐   Freeze-dried ☐

Flavor/Texture: _____

Shelf Life _____

Observations _____

_____

_____

Annual Edible Plant Log

Plant _____ Variety _____ Hybrid ☐ Heirloom ☐ Open-Pollinated ☐

Disease Resistance_____Seed ☐ Transplant ☐ Cutting ☐

Date Acquired:_____Source: _____

Germination Stage

Water Requirements:_____Light Requirements:_____Feeding Schedule:_____

Foliage Development Stage

Water Requirements:_____Light Requirements:_____Feeding Schedule:_____

Flowering

Water Requirements:_____Light Requirements:_____Feeding Schedule:_____

Fruiting

Water Requirements:_____Light Requirements:_____Feeding Schedule:_____

	Date	Notes & Observations		Date	Notes & Observations
Sown			Week 10:		
Planted			Week 11:		
Week 1:			Week 12:		
Week 2:			Week 13:		
Week 3:			Week 14:		
Week 4:			Week 15:		
Week 5:			Week 16:		
Week 6:			Week 17:		
Week 7:			Week 18:		
Week 8:			Week 19:		
Week 9:			Week 20:		
Harvest:					

Storage Notes: Fresh ☐ Canned ☐ Dried ☐ Frozen ☐ Freeze-dried ☐

Flavor/Texture: _____

Shelf Life _____

Observations _____

_____

_____

Annual Edible Plant Log

Plant _____ Variety _____ Hybrid ☐ Heirloom ☐ Open-Pollinated ☐

Disease Resistance _____ Seed ☐ Transplant ☐ Cutting ☐

Date Acquired: _____ Source: _____

Germination Stage

Water Requirements: _____ Light Requirements: _____ Feeding Schedule: _____

Foliage Development Stage

Water Requirements: _____ Light Requirements: _____ Feeding Schedule: _____

Flowering

Water Requirements: _____ Light Requirements: _____ Feeding Schedule: _____

Fruiting

Water Requirements: _____ Light Requirements: _____ Feeding Schedule: _____

	Date	Notes & Observations		Date	Notes & Observations
Sown			Week 10:		
Planted			Week 11:		
Week 1:			Week 12:		
Week 2:			Week 13:		
Week 3:			Week 14:		
Week 4:			Week 15:		
Week 5:			Week 16:		
Week 6:			Week 17:		
Week 7:			Week 18:		
Week 8:			Week 19:		
Week 9:			Week 20:		
Harvest:					

Storage Notes: Fresh ☐ Canned ☐ Dried ☐ Frozen ☐ Freeze-dried ☐

Flavor/Texture: _____

Shelf Life _____

Observations _____

_____

_____

Annual Edible Plant Log

Plant _____ Variety _____ Hybrid ☐ Heirloom ☐ Open-Pollinated ☐

Disease Resistance_____Seed ☐ Transplant ☐ Cutting ☐

Date Acquired:_____Source: _____

Germination Stage

Water Requirements:_____Light Requirements:_____Feeding Schedule:_____

Foliage Development Stage

Water Requirements:_____Light Requirements:_____Feeding Schedule:_____

Flowering

Water Requirements:_____Light Requirements:_____Feeding Schedule:_____

Fruiting

Water Requirements:_____Light Requirements:_____Feeding Schedule:_____

	Date	Notes & Observations		Date	Notes & Observations
Sown			Week 10:		
Planted			Week 11:		
Week 1:			Week 12:		
Week 2:			Week 13:		
Week 3:			Week 14:		
Week 4:			Week 15:		
Week 5:			Week 16:		
Week 6:			Week 17:		
Week 7:			Week 18:		
Week 8:			Week 19:		
Week 9:			Week 20:		
Harvest:					

Storage Notes: Fresh ☐   Canned ☐   Dried ☐   Frozen ☐   Freeze-dried ☐

Flavor/Texture: _____

Shelf Life _____

Observations _____

_____

_____

Annual Edible Plant Log

Plant _____ Variety _____ Hybrid ☐ Heirloom ☐ Open-Pollinated ☐

Disease Resistance_____Seed ☐ Transplant ☐ Cutting ☐

Date Acquired:_____Source: _____

Germination Stage

Water Requirements:_____Light Requirements:_____Feeding Schedule:_____

Foliage Development Stage

Water Requirements:_____Light Requirements:_____Feeding Schedule:_____

Flowering

Water Requirements:_____Light Requirements:_____Feeding Schedule:_____

Fruiting

Water Requirements:_____Light Requirements:_____Feeding Schedule:_____

	Date	Notes & Observations		Date	Notes & Observations
Sown			Week 10:		
Planted			Week 11:		
Week 1:			Week 12:		
Week 2:			Week 13:		
Week 3:			Week 14:		
Week 4:			Week 15:		
Week 5:			Week 16:		
Week 6:			Week 17:		
Week 7:			Week 18:		
Week 8:			Week 19:		
Week 9:			Week 20:		
Harvest:					

Storage Notes: Fresh ☐   Canned ☐   Dried ☐   Frozen ☐   Freeze-dried ☐

Flavor/Texture: _____

Shelf Life _____

Observations _____

_____

_____

Perennial Edible Plant Log

Plant_____ Variety_____ Tree ☐ Bush ☐ Vine ☐ Plant ☐

Disease Resistance_____Seed ☐ Transplant ☐ Cutting ☐

Date Acquired:_____Source: _____

Germination Stage

Water Requirements:_____Light Requirements:_____Feeding Schedule:_____

Foliage Development Stage

Water Requirements:_____Light Requirements:_____Feeding Schedule:_____

Flowering

Water Requirements:_____Light Requirements:_____Feeding Schedule:_____

Fruiting

Water Requirements:_____Light Requirements:_____Feeding Schedule:_____

	Date	Notes & Observations		Date	Notes & Observations
Sown			Month 7:		
Planted			Month 8:		
Week 1:			Month 9:		
Week 2:			Month 10:		
Week 3:			Month 11:		
Week 4:			Month 12:		
Month 2:			Month 13:		
Month 3:			Month 14:		
Month 4:			Month 15:		
Month 5:			Month 16:		
Month 6:					

Pest Risks: _____

Pest Treatment: _____

Disease Risk: _____

Disease Treatment: _____

Overall Observations:

_____

_____

_____

Perennial Edible Plant Log

Plant_____ Variety_____ Tree ☐ Bush ☐ Vine ☐ Plant ☐

Disease Resistance_____Seed ☐ Transplant ☐ Cutting ☐

Date Acquired:_____Source: _____

Germination Stage

Water Requirements:_____Light Requirements:_____Feeding Schedule:_____

Foliage Development Stage

Water Requirements:_____Light Requirements:_____Feeding Schedule:_____

Flowering

Water Requirements:_____Light Requirements:_____Feeding Schedule:_____

Fruiting

Water Requirements:_____Light Requirements:_____Feeding Schedule:_____

	Date	Notes & Observations		Date	Notes & Observations
Sown			Month 7:		
Planted			Month 8:		
Week 1:			Month 9:		
Week 2:			Month 10:		
Week 3:			Month 11:		
Week 4:			Month 12:		
Month 2:			Month 13:		
Month 3:			Month 14:		
Month 4:			Month 15:		
Month 5:			Month 16:		
Month 6:					

Pest Risks: _____

Pest Treatment: _____

Disease Risk: _____

Disease Treatment: _____

Overall Observations:

_____

_____

_____

Perennial Edible Plant Log

Plant_____ Variety_____ Tree ☐ Bush ☐ Vine ☐ Plant ☐

Disease Resistance_____Seed ☐ Transplant ☐ Cutting ☐

Date Acquired:_____Source: _____

Germination Stage

Water Requirements:_____Light Requirements:_____Feeding Schedule:_____

Foliage Development Stage

Water Requirements:_____Light Requirements:_____Feeding Schedule:_____

Flowering

Water Requirements:_____Light Requirements:_____Feeding Schedule:_____

Fruiting

Water Requirements:_____Light Requirements:_____Feeding Schedule:_____

	Date	Notes & Observations		Date	Notes & Observations
Sown			Month 7:		
Planted			Month 8:		
Week 1:			Month 9:		
Week 2:			Month 10:		
Week 3:			Month 11:		
Week 4:			Month 12:		
Month 2:			Month 13:		
Month 3:			Month 14:		
Month 4:			Month 15:		
Month 5:			Month 16:		
Month 6:					

Pest Risks: _____

Pest Treatment: _____

Disease Risk: _____

Disease Treatment: _____

Overall Observations:

_____

_____

_____

Perennial Edible Plant Log

Plant_____ Variety_____ Tree ☐ Bush ☐ Vine ☐ Plant ☐

Disease Resistance_____Seed ☐ Transplant ☐ Cutting ☐

Date Acquired:_____Source: _____

Germination Stage

Water Requirements:_____Light Requirements:_____Feeding Schedule:_____

Foliage Development Stage

Water Requirements:_____Light Requirements:_____Feeding Schedule:_____

Flowering

Water Requirements:_____Light Requirements:_____Feeding Schedule:_____

Fruiting

Water Requirements:_____Light Requirements:_____Feeding Schedule:_____

	Date	Notes & Observations		Date	Notes & Observations
Sown			Month 7:		
Planted			Month 8:		
Week 1:			Month 9:		
Week 2:			Month 10:		
Week 3:			Month 11:		
Week 4:			Month 12:		
Month 2:			Month 13:		
Month 3:			Month 14:		
Month 4:			Month 15:		
Month 5:			Month 16:		
Month 6:					

Pest Risks: _____

Pest Treatment: _____

Disease Risk: _____

Disease Treatment: _____

Overall Observations:

_____

_____

_____

Perennial Edible Plant Log

Plant_____ Variety_____ Tree ☐ Bush ☐ Vine ☐ Plant ☐

Disease Resistance_____Seed ☐ Transplant ☐ Cutting ☐

Date Acquired:_____Source: _____

Germination Stage

Water Requirements:_____Light Requirements:_____Feeding Schedule:_____

Foliage Development Stage

Water Requirements:_____Light Requirements:_____Feeding Schedule:_____

Flowering

Water Requirements:_____Light Requirements:_____Feeding Schedule:_____

Fruiting

Water Requirements:_____Light Requirements:_____Feeding Schedule:_____

	Date	Notes & Observations		Date	Notes & Observations
Sown			Month 7:		
Planted			Month 8:		
Week 1:			Month 9:		
Week 2:			Month 10:		
Week 3:			Month 11:		
Week 4:			Month 12:		
Month 2:			Month 13:		
Month 3:			Month 14:		
Month 4:			Month 15:		
Month 5:			Month 16:		
Month 6:					

Pest Risks: _____

Pest Treatment: _____

Disease Risk: _____

Disease Treatment: _____

Overall Observations:

_____

_____

_____

Perennial Edible Plant Log

Plant_____ Variety_____ Tree ☐ Bush ☐ Vine ☐ Plant ☐

Disease Resistance_____Seed ☐ Transplant ☐ Cutting ☐

Date Acquired:_____Source: _____

Germination Stage

Water Requirements:_____Light Requirements:_____Feeding Schedule:_____

Foliage Development Stage

Water Requirements:_____Light Requirements:_____Feeding Schedule:_____

Flowering

Water Requirements:_____Light Requirements:_____Feeding Schedule:_____

Fruiting

Water Requirements:_____Light Requirements:_____Feeding Schedule:_____

	Date	Notes & Observations		Date	Notes & Observations
Sown			Month 7:		
Planted			Month 8:		
Week 1:			Month 9:		
Week 2:			Month 10:		
Week 3:			Month 11:		
Week 4:			Month 12:		
Month 2:			Month 13:		
Month 3:			Month 14:		
Month 4:			Month 15:		
Month 5:			Month 16:		
Month 6:					

Pest Risks: _____

Pest Treatment: _____

Disease Risk: _____

Disease Treatment: _____

Overall Observations:

_____

_____

_____

Perennial Edible Plant Log

Plant_____ Variety_____ Tree ☐ Bush ☐ Vine ☐ Plant ☐

Disease Resistance_____Seed ☐ Transplant ☐ Cutting ☐

Date Acquired:_____Source: _____

Germination Stage

Water Requirements:_____Light Requirements:_____Feeding Schedule:_____

Foliage Development Stage

Water Requirements:_____Light Requirements:_____Feeding Schedule:_____

Flowering

Water Requirements:_____Light Requirements:_____Feeding Schedule:_____

Fruiting

Water Requirements:_____Light Requirements:_____Feeding Schedule:_____

	Date	Notes & Observations		Date	Notes & Observations
Sown			Month 7:		
Planted			Month 8:		
Week 1:			Month 9:		
Week 2:			Month 10:		
Week 3:			Month 11:		
Week 4:			Month 12:		
Month 2:			Month 13:		
Month 3:			Month 14:		
Month 4:			Month 15:		
Month 5:			Month 16:		
Month 6:					

Pest Risks: _____

Pest Treatment: _____

Disease Risk: _____

Disease Treatment: _____

Overall Observations:

_____

_____

_____

Perennial Edible Plant Log

Plant_____ Variety_____ Tree ☐ Bush ☐ Vine ☐ Plant ☐

Disease Resistance_____Seed ☐ Transplant ☐ Cutting ☐

Date Acquired:_____Source: _____

Germination Stage

Water Requirements:_____Light Requirements:_____Feeding Schedule:_____

Foliage Development Stage

Water Requirements:_____Light Requirements:_____Feeding Schedule:_____

Flowering

Water Requirements:_____Light Requirements:_____Feeding Schedule:_____

Fruiting

Water Requirements:_____Light Requirements:_____Feeding Schedule:_____

	Date	Notes & Observations		Date	Notes & Observations
Sown			Month 7:		
Planted			Month 8:		
Week 1:			Month 9:		
Week 2:			Month 10:		
Week 3:			Month 11:		
Week 4:			Month 12:		
Month 2:			Month 13:		
Month 3:			Month 14:		
Month 4:			Month 15:		
Month 5:			Month 16:		
Month 6:					

Pest Risks: _____

Pest Treatment: _____

Disease Risk: _____

Disease Treatment: _____

Overall Observations:

_____

_____

_____

Perennial Edible Plant Log

Plant_____ Variety_____ Tree ☐ Bush ☐ Vine ☐ Plant ☐

Disease Resistance_____Seed ☐ Transplant ☐ Cutting ☐

Date Acquired:_____Source: _____

Germination Stage

Water Requirements:_____Light Requirements:_____Feeding Schedule:_____

Foliage Development Stage

Water Requirements:_____Light Requirements:_____Feeding Schedule:_____

Flowering

Water Requirements:_____Light Requirements:_____Feeding Schedule:_____

Fruiting

Water Requirements:_____Light Requirements:_____Feeding Schedule:_____

	Date	Notes & Observations		Date	Notes & Observations
Sown			Month 7:		
Planted			Month 8:		
Week 1:			Month 9:		
Week 2:			Month 10:		
Week 3:			Month 11:		
Week 4:			Month 12:		
Month 2:			Month 13:		
Month 3:			Month 14:		
Month 4:			Month 15:		
Month 5:			Month 16:		
Month 6:					

Pest Risks: _____

Pest Treatment: _____

Disease Risk: _____

Disease Treatment: _____

Overall Observations:

_____

_____

_____

Perennial Edible Plant Log

Plant_____ Variety_____ Tree ☐ Bush ☐ Vine ☐ Plant ☐

Disease Resistance_____Seed ☐ Transplant ☐ Cutting ☐

Date Acquired:_____Source: _____

Germination Stage

Water Requirements:_____Light Requirements:_____Feeding Schedule:_____

Foliage Development Stage

Water Requirements:_____Light Requirements:_____Feeding Schedule:_____

Flowering

Water Requirements:_____Light Requirements:_____Feeding Schedule:_____

Fruiting

Water Requirements:_____Light Requirements:_____Feeding Schedule:_____

	Date	Notes & Observations		Date	Notes & Observations
Sown			Month 7:		
Planted			Month 8:		
Week 1:			Month 9:		
Week 2:			Month 10:		
Week 3:			Month 11:		
Week 4:			Month 12:		
Month 2:			Month 13:		
Month 3:			Month 14:		
Month 4:			Month 15:		
Month 5:			Month 16:		
Month 6:					

Pest Risks: _____

Pest Treatment: _____

Disease Risk: _____

Disease Treatment: _____

Overall Observations:

_____

_____

_____

Perennial Edible Plant Log

Plant_____ Variety_____ Tree ☐ Bush ☐ Vine ☐ Plant ☐

Disease Resistance_____Seed ☐ Transplant ☐ Cutting ☐

Date Acquired:_____Source: _____

Germination Stage

Water Requirements:_____Light Requirements:_____Feeding Schedule:_____

Foliage Development Stage

Water Requirements:_____Light Requirements:_____Feeding Schedule:_____

Flowering

Water Requirements:_____Light Requirements:_____Feeding Schedule:_____

Fruiting

Water Requirements:_____Light Requirements:_____Feeding Schedule:_____

	Date	Notes & Observations		Date	Notes & Observations
Sown			Month 7:		
Planted			Month 8:		
Week 1:			Month 9:		
Week 2:			Month 10:		
Week 3:			Month 11:		
Week 4:			Month 12:		
Month 2:			Month 13:		
Month 3:			Month 14:		
Month 4:			Month 15:		
Month 5:			Month 16:		
Month 6:					

Pest Risks: _____

Pest Treatment: _____

Disease Risk: _____

Disease Treatment: _____

Overall Observations:

_____

_____

_____

Perennial Edible Plant Log

Plant_____ Variety_____ Tree ☐ Bush ☐ Vine ☐ Plant ☐

Disease Resistance_____Seed ☐ Transplant ☐ Cutting ☐

Date Acquired:_____Source: _____

Germination Stage

Water Requirements:_____Light Requirements:_____Feeding Schedule:_____

Foliage Development Stage

Water Requirements:_____Light Requirements:_____Feeding Schedule:_____

Flowering

Water Requirements:_____Light Requirements:_____Feeding Schedule:_____

Fruiting

Water Requirements:_____Light Requirements:_____Feeding Schedule:_____

	Date	Notes & Observations		Date	Notes & Observations
Sown			Month 7:		
Planted			Month 8:		
Week 1:			Month 9:		
Week 2:			Month 10:		
Week 3:			Month 11:		
Week 4:			Month 12:		
Month 2:			Month 13:		
Month 3:			Month 14:		
Month 4:			Month 15:		
Month 5:			Month 16:		
Month 6:					

Pest Risks: _____

Pest Treatment: _____

Disease Risk: _____

Disease Treatment: _____

Overall Observations:

_____

_____

_____

Perennial Edible Plant Log

Plant_____ Variety_____ Tree ☐ Bush ☐ Vine ☐ Plant ☐

Disease Resistance_____Seed ☐ Transplant ☐ Cutting ☐

Date Acquired:_____Source: _____

Germination Stage

Water Requirements:_____Light Requirements:_____Feeding Schedule:_____

Foliage Development Stage

Water Requirements:_____Light Requirements:_____Feeding Schedule:_____

Flowering

Water Requirements:_____Light Requirements:_____Feeding Schedule:_____

Fruiting

Water Requirements:_____Light Requirements:_____Feeding Schedule:_____

	Date	Notes & Observations		Date	Notes & Observations
Sown			Month 7:		
Planted			Month 8:		
Week 1:			Month 9:		
Week 2:			Month 10:		
Week 3:			Month 11:		
Week 4:			Month 12:		
Month 2:			Month 13:		
Month 3:			Month 14:		
Month 4:			Month 15:		
Month 5:			Month 16:		
Month 6:					

Pest Risks: _____

Pest Treatment: _____

Disease Risk: _____

Disease Treatment: _____

Overall Observations:

_____

_____

_____

Perennial Edible Plant Log

Plant_____ Variety_____ Tree ☐ Bush ☐ Vine ☐ Plant ☐

Disease Resistance_____Seed ☐ Transplant ☐ Cutting ☐

Date Acquired:_____Source: _____

Germination Stage

Water Requirements:_____Light Requirements:_____Feeding Schedule:_____

Foliage Development Stage

Water Requirements:_____Light Requirements:_____Feeding Schedule:_____

Flowering

Water Requirements:_____Light Requirements:_____Feeding Schedule:_____

Fruiting

Water Requirements:_____Light Requirements:_____Feeding Schedule:_____

	Date	Notes & Observations		Date	Notes & Observations
Sown			Month 7:		
Planted			Month 8:		
Week 1:			Month 9:		
Week 2:			Month 10:		
Week 3:			Month 11:		
Week 4:			Month 12:		
Month 2:			Month 13:		
Month 3:			Month 14:		
Month 4:			Month 15:		
Month 5:			Month 16:		
Month 6:					

Pest Risks: _____

Pest Treatment: _____

Disease Risk: _____

Disease Treatment: _____

Overall Observations:

_____

_____

_____

Perennial Edible Plant Log

Plant_____ Variety_____ Tree ☐ Bush ☐ Vine ☐ Plant ☐

Disease Resistance_____Seed ☐ Transplant ☐ Cutting ☐

Date Acquired:_____Source: _____

Germination Stage

Water Requirements:_____Light Requirements:_____Feeding Schedule:_____

Foliage Development Stage

Water Requirements:_____Light Requirements:_____Feeding Schedule:_____

Flowering

Water Requirements:_____Light Requirements:_____Feeding Schedule:_____

Fruiting

Water Requirements:_____Light Requirements:_____Feeding Schedule:_____

	Date	Notes & Observations		Date	Notes & Observations
Sown			Month 7:		
Planted			Month 8:		
Week 1:			Month 9:		
Week 2:			Month 10:		
Week 3:			Month 11:		
Week 4:			Month 12:		
Month 2:			Month 13:		
Month 3:			Month 14:		
Month 4:			Month 15:		
Month 5:			Month 16:		
Month 6:					

Pest Risks: _____

Pest Treatment: _____

Disease Risk: _____

Disease Treatment: _____

Overall Observations:

_____

_____

_____

Perennial Edible Plant Log

Plant_____ Variety_____ Tree ☐ Bush ☐ Vine ☐ Plant ☐

Disease Resistance_____Seed ☐ Transplant ☐ Cutting ☐

Date Acquired:_____Source: _____

Germination Stage

Water Requirements:_____Light Requirements:_____Feeding Schedule:_____

Foliage Development Stage

Water Requirements:_____Light Requirements:_____Feeding Schedule:_____

Flowering

Water Requirements:_____Light Requirements:_____Feeding Schedule:_____

Fruiting

Water Requirements:_____Light Requirements:_____Feeding Schedule:_____

	Date	Notes & Observations		Date	Notes & Observations
Sown			Month 7:		
Planted			Month 8:		
Week 1:			Month 9:		
Week 2:			Month 10:		
Week 3:			Month 11:		
Week 4:			Month 12:		
Month 2:			Month 13:		
Month 3:			Month 14:		
Month 4:			Month 15:		
Month 5:			Month 16:		
Month 6:					

Pest Risks: _____

Pest Treatment: _____

Disease Risk: _____

Disease Treatment: _____

Overall Observations:

_____

_____

_____

Perennial Edible Plant Log

Plant_____ Variety_____ Tree ☐ Bush ☐ Vine ☐ Plant ☐

Disease Resistance_____Seed ☐ Transplant ☐ Cutting ☐

Date Acquired:_____Source: _____

Germination Stage

Water Requirements:_____Light Requirements:_____Feeding Schedule:_____

Foliage Development Stage

Water Requirements:_____Light Requirements:_____Feeding Schedule:_____

Flowering

Water Requirements:_____Light Requirements:_____Feeding Schedule:_____

Fruiting

Water Requirements:_____Light Requirements:_____Feeding Schedule:_____

	Date	Notes & Observations		Date	Notes & Observations
Sown			Month 7:		
Planted			Month 8:		
Week 1:			Month 9:		
Week 2:			Month 10:		
Week 3:			Month 11:		
Week 4:			Month 12:		
Month 2:			Month 13:		
Month 3:			Month 14:		
Month 4:			Month 15:		
Month 5:			Month 16:		
Month 6:					

Pest Risks: _____

Pest Treatment: _____

Disease Risk: _____

Disease Treatment: _____

Overall Observations:

_____

_____

_____

Perennial Edible Plant Log

Plant_____ Variety_____ Tree ☐ Bush ☐ Vine ☐ Plant ☐

Disease Resistance_____Seed ☐ Transplant ☐ Cutting ☐

Date Acquired:_____Source: _____

Germination Stage

Water Requirements:_____Light Requirements:_____Feeding Schedule:_____

Foliage Development Stage

Water Requirements:_____Light Requirements:_____Feeding Schedule:_____

Flowering

Water Requirements:_____Light Requirements:_____Feeding Schedule:_____

Fruiting

Water Requirements:_____Light Requirements:_____Feeding Schedule:_____

	Date	Notes & Observations		Date	Notes & Observations
Sown			Month 7:		
Planted			Month 8:		
Week 1:			Month 9:		
Week 2:			Month 10:		
Week 3:			Month 11:		
Week 4:			Month 12:		
Month 2:			Month 13:		
Month 3:			Month 14:		
Month 4:			Month 15:		
Month 5:			Month 16:		
Month 6:					

Pest Risks: _____

Pest Treatment: _____

Disease Risk: _____

Disease Treatment: _____

Overall Observations:

_____

_____

_____

Perennial Edible Plant Log

Plant_____ Variety_____ Tree ☐ Bush ☐ Vine ☐ Plant ☐

Disease Resistance_____Seed ☐ Transplant ☐ Cutting ☐

Date Acquired:_____Source: _____

Germination Stage

Water Requirements:_____Light Requirements:_____Feeding Schedule:_____

Foliage Development Stage

Water Requirements:_____Light Requirements:_____Feeding Schedule:_____

Flowering

Water Requirements:_____Light Requirements:_____Feeding Schedule:_____

Fruiting

Water Requirements:_____Light Requirements:_____Feeding Schedule:_____

	Date	Notes & Observations		Date	Notes & Observations
Sown			Month 7:		
Planted			Month 8:		
Week 1:			Month 9:		
Week 2:			Month 10:		
Week 3:			Month 11:		
Week 4:			Month 12:		
Month 2:			Month 13:		
Month 3:			Month 14:		
Month 4:			Month 15:		
Month 5:			Month 16:		
Month 6:					

Pest Risks: _____

Pest Treatment: _____

Disease Risk: _____

Disease Treatment: _____

Overall Observations:

_____

_____

_____

Perennial Edible Plant Log

Plant_____ Variety_____ Tree ☐ Bush ☐ Vine ☐ Plant ☐

Disease Resistance_____Seed ☐ Transplant ☐ Cutting ☐

Date Acquired:_____Source: _____

Germination Stage

Water Requirements:_____Light Requirements:_____Feeding Schedule:_____

Foliage Development Stage

Water Requirements:_____Light Requirements:_____Feeding Schedule:_____

Flowering

Water Requirements:_____Light Requirements:_____Feeding Schedule:_____

Fruiting

Water Requirements:_____Light Requirements:_____Feeding Schedule:_____

	Date	Notes & Observations		Date	Notes & Observations
Sown			Month 7:		
Planted			Month 8:		
Week 1:			Month 9:		
Week 2:			Month 10:		
Week 3:			Month 11:		
Week 4:			Month 12:		
Month 2:			Month 13:		
Month 3:			Month 14:		
Month 4:			Month 15:		
Month 5:			Month 16:		
Month 6:					

Pest Risks: _____

Pest Treatment: _____

Disease Risk: _____

Disease Treatment: _____

Overall Observations:

_____

_____

_____

Perennial Edible Plant Log

Plant_____ Variety_____ Tree ☐ Bush ☐ Vine ☐ Plant ☐

Disease Resistance_____Seed ☐ Transplant ☐ Cutting ☐

Date Acquired:_____Source: _____

Germination Stage

Water Requirements:_____Light Requirements:_____Feeding Schedule:_____

Foliage Development Stage

Water Requirements:_____Light Requirements:_____Feeding Schedule:_____

Flowering

Water Requirements:_____Light Requirements:_____Feeding Schedule:_____

Fruiting

Water Requirements:_____Light Requirements:_____Feeding Schedule:_____

	Date	Notes & Observations		Date	Notes & Observations
Sown			Month 7:		
Planted			Month 8:		
Week 1:			Month 9:		
Week 2:			Month 10:		
Week 3:			Month 11:		
Week 4:			Month 12:		
Month 2:			Month 13:		
Month 3:			Month 14:		
Month 4:			Month 15:		
Month 5:			Month 16:		
Month 6:					

Pest Risks: _____

Pest Treatment: _____

Disease Risk: _____

Disease Treatment: _____

Overall Observations:

_____

_____

_____

Perennial Edible Plant Log

Plant_____ Variety_____ Tree ☐ Bush ☐ Vine ☐ Plant ☐

Disease Resistance_____Seed ☐ Transplant ☐ Cutting ☐

Date Acquired:_____Source: _____

Germination Stage

Water Requirements:_____Light Requirements:_____Feeding Schedule:_____

Foliage Development Stage

Water Requirements:_____Light Requirements:_____Feeding Schedule:_____

Flowering

Water Requirements:_____Light Requirements:_____Feeding Schedule:_____

Fruiting

Water Requirements:_____Light Requirements:_____Feeding Schedule:_____

	Date	Notes & Observations		Date	Notes & Observations
Sown			Month 7:		
Planted			Month 8:		
Week 1:			Month 9:		
Week 2:			Month 10:		
Week 3:			Month 11:		
Week 4:			Month 12:		
Month 2:			Month 13:		
Month 3:			Month 14:		
Month 4:			Month 15:		
Month 5:			Month 16:		
Month 6:					

Pest Risks: _____

Pest Treatment: _____

Disease Risk: _____

Disease Treatment: _____

Overall Observations:

_____

_____

_____

Suppliers List

Products	Address	Website / Email	Phone

Suppliers List

Products	Address	Website / Email	Phone

Suppliers List

Products	Address	Website / Email	Phone

RESOURCES

KEY TO PLANT TYPES

To save space, some recommended edible plants have been grouped together because they are all good choices to plant for that particular month. This is a key to those groups:

Asian Cabbage	Chili Peppers	Peas	Southern Peas
bok choi cabbage blues Chinese cabbage choy sum Japanese cabbage napa Cabbage pak choi	Aji Dulce Anaheim peppers cayenne peppers cubanelle peppers datil peppers Fresno peppers habaneros jalapeños Padron peppers poblanos serrano peppers shishito peppers Thai peppers	English peas Snow peas Snap peas	black-eyed peas cowpeas cream peas crowder peas field peas purple hull peas
Summer Squash	Sweet Peppers	Tropical Spinach	Winter Squash
cousa squash crookneck squash patty-pan squash tatume squash yellow straightneck squash zucchini	banana peppers bell peppers pepperoncini peppers	callaloo Egyptian spinach longevity spinach Malabar spinach Okinawa spinach sissoo Surname spinach vegetable amaranth water spinach	acorn squash banana squash Blue Hubbard squash buttercup squash butternut squash carnival squash delicata squash kabocha squash pie pumpkins spaghetti squash sweet dumpling squash turban squash

First and Last Frost Dates for 2023

Your first frost dates indicates average first day your area experienced a light freeze. That doesn't mean you won't experience a freeze before then, just that the chances are only about 30%. Likewise, your last frost date is the average last day of a light freeze, and afterward, the chance of one is only about 30%.

North Louisiana / Zone 8

First Frost   Nov 13

Last Frost   Mar 14

South Louisiana / Zone 9

First Frost   Dec 30

Last Frost   Feb 8

Coastal Louisiana / Zone 10

First Frost   N/A

Last Frost   N/A

Types of Frosts and Freezes

When it comes to farming or gardening, frosts and freezes are categorized as follows:

A **Frost** is when temperatures drop to between 33 and 36 degrees Fahrenheit. This can kill off some cold-tender annual plants, and often results in leaf damage. When the humidity is high during a frost, ice crystals can form on the surface of the leaves, causing damage to the plants.

A **Light Freeze** is 29 to 32 degrees Fahrenheit. Tender annual plants may be killed, and hardier plants may suffer damage to the foliage.

A **Moderate Freeze** is 25 to 28 degrees Fahrenheit, which will kill off hardier annuals and tender perennials and may inflict damage on hardy perennials.

A **Severe Freeze** is anything below 24 degrees Fahrenheit, which is likely to kill off any annual plants, even the cold-hardy ones. Perennials will suffer extensive damage to foliage.

In hardier plants or those in protected areas of the garden, plant damage may not occur unless the temperatures dip for more than five hours. For small seedlings or those exposed to high winds, however, damage can take place if the thermometer drops for as little as an hour.

SAVING YOUR PLANTS

One of the trickier parts of Louisiana gardening is working with the variable winter temperatures. Nearly all parts of Louisiana will experience temperatures below the freezing point during the winter. However, these temperatures may last no more than an hour in many parts of the state.

Keeping an eye on the forecast is advised. Most freezes occur during the early hours of the morning, when the temperature reaches its lowest point. However, even heat-loving garden vegetables like tomatoes and peppers can be easily protected during any frost to moderate freeze with some preparation.

When a cold snap is predicted, water any sensitive vegetable plants well the day before to ensure they're well hydrated.

Providing adequate mulch cover over the roots will help keep them warm.

Cover plants well before sunset in order to trap in any heat from sunlight.

Use frost cloth, blankets, or even old sheets to cover the plant. Choose covers that are large enough to reach the ground.

Avoid using plastic, which can damage plants where touching the foliage.

Remove coverings as soon as possible after sunrise.

Soil Temperature Requirements for Seed Germination

While you may note the last frost date in your zone and plan your seed sowing around the calendar, another factor to check is the soil temperature. Most vegetables will germination at soil temperatures between 60 and 70 degrees Fahrenheit. However, a few cool-season crops will germinate at temperatures as low as 40 to 50 degrees.

Louisiana temperatures are generally conducive to seed germination, however, December and January, especially in North Louisiana, can prove quite cold. Low temperatures combined with wet soil often results in seed that rots before it can germinate.

Also, many vegetable seeds also have a maximum temperature, and many won't germinate at over 95 degrees. With hot sun baking bare soil, it's not difficult to see why summer can be the wrong time to sow seed in Louisiana.

Noting the optimal temperature for germination for each vegetable you're trying to grow will help you provide the best conditions for healthy plants. It can also help you get a head start on spring planting, as you can easily moderate temperatures in your home or greenhouse to produce strong starts ready for planting out in early spring.

Understanding the temperature tolerance for various seeds also reveals opportunities to add plants to your garden you may not have considered. You can remain flexible to unexpected weather by using soil temperatures to inform your planting decisions. Understanding how temperatures affect seed germination can also give you the confidence to experiment more in your gardening.

TEMPERATURES FOR FLOWER SEED

Flower Seed	Optimal Temps	Flower Seed	Optimal Temps	Flower Seed	Optimal Temps	Flower Seed	Optimal Temps
Alyssum	55-70	Daisies	65-70	Lupine	55-65	Roselle	75-85
Angelonia	70-75	Delphinium	60-68	Milkweed	70-75	Rudbeckia	70-75
Aster	65-70	Dianthus	60-68	Monarda	60-70	Salvias	70-75
Bachelor Button	65-70	Four o' Clocks	65-70	Moonflower	85-95	Snapdragon	60-70
Blanket Flower	70-75	Foxgloves	60-65	Morning Glory	70-85	Statice	68-75
Borage	65-85	French Marigold	70-75	Nasturtium	65-70	Stocks	60-65
California Poppy	55-60	Geranium	70-75	Nicotiana	70-75	Strawflower	70-75
Canna	70-85	Gomphrena	70	Nigella	65-70	Sunflower	70-85
Celosia	70-75	Hollyhocks	60-70	Pansy	65-70	Tithonia	70-75
Coleus	70-75	Impatiens	70-75	Petunia	70-80	Verbena	70-75
Coneflower	65-70	Liatris	55-72	Phlox	60-65	Vinca	70-75
Coreopsis	55-75	Lisianthis	75	Portulaca	75-85	Yarrow	65-75
Dahlia	70-80	Lobelia	65-75	Red Poppy	65-70	Zinnia	70-80

TEMPERATURES FOR VEGETABLE SEED

Vegetable Plant	Minimum Temperature	Optimal Germination Temperatures	Maximum Temperature
Beans	60	75-85	95
Beets	40	65-85	95
Broccoli	40	60-85	95
Cabbage	40	60-85	95
Cantaloupe	60	75-85	105
Carrots	40	65-85	95
Cauliflower	40	65-85	95
Corn	50	65-95	105
Cucumbers	60	65-95	105
Eggplant	60	75-85	95
Garlic	32	65-85	95
Leeks	32	60-75	85
Lettuce	32	60-75	85
Okra	60	85-95	105
Onions	32	65-85	95
Parsley	40	65-85	95
Parsnips	32	65-75	85
Peas	40	65-75	85
Peppers	60	65-75	95
Pumpkins	60	85-95	105
Radish	40	65-85	95
Spinach	32	65-75	75
Squash	60	85-95	105
Swiss Chard	40	65-85	95
Tomatoes	50	65-85	95
Turnips	40	60-95	105
Watermelon	60	75-95	105

BEST VEGETABLE VARIETIES FOR LOUISIANA

Beans, Bush		Beans, Climbing	Beans, Shelling/Storage	Beets
Ambra	Green Crop	Blue Lake	Christmas	Avalanche
Blue Lake 274	Hialeah	Kentucky Blue-AAS	Dixie Speckled	Boro
Bronco	Lynx	Kentucky Wonder 191	Butterpea.	Chariot
Caprice	Magnum	La Purple	Eastland	Chioggia
Carson	Maxibel	Louisiana Purple Pod	Florida Speckled	Detroit Dark Red
Cherokee Wax	Provider	McCaslan	Fordhook 242 (AAS)	Early Wonder Tall Top
Contender	Roma II	Northeaster	Henderson Bush	Golden Detroit
Derby	Royal Burgundy	Rattlesnake	Jackson Wonder	Red Ace
Dusky	Storm	State	King of Garden	Red Cloud
Festina	Strike	Volunteer	Thorogreen (DM)	Ruby Queen
Gold Rush	Tendergreen	Yardlong Asparagus Bean	White Dixie Butterpea	Touchstone Gold
Golden Rod	Topcrop		Willow Leaf	
Golden Wax	Valentino			

Broccoli, Heading	Broccoli, Flowering	Cabbage		
Arcadia	Calabrese	Blue Dynasty	Green Boy	Round Dutch
Bay Meadows	De Cicco	Blue Thunder	Green Cup	Royal Vantage
Castle Dome	Piracicaba	Blue Vantage	Platinum Dynasty	Savoy
Diplomat		Bravo	Quick Start	Savoy Ace
Emerald Crown		Capture	Quista	Solid Blue 780
Emerald Pride		Cheers	Red Acre	Stonehead
Everest		Clarissa	Red Dynasty	Superstar
Green Magic		Copenhagen	Red Express	Tendersweet
Gypsy		Emblem	Red Hawk	Vantage Point
Marathon		Famosa	Red Jewel	Wakefield
Packman		Fast Vantage	Rio Grand	
Patriot	**Brussels Sprouts**	Flat Dutch	Rio Verde	
Patron	Jade Cross E	Golden Acre		
Premium Crop	Long Island Improved			
Southern Comet	Oliver			
Triathlon				
Waltham				
Windsor				

Cabbage, Asian	Cantaloupe	Carrots	Cauliflower	Collards
Bilko	Ambrosia	Apache	Bermeo	Blue Max
Bopak	Aphrodite	Chantenay Red Core	Candid Charm	Bulldog
Cabbage Blues	Athena	Danvers 126	Cheddar	Champion
China Express	Caravelle	Danvers Half Long	Cumberland	Flash
Emiko	Gold Strike	Deep Purple	Flamenco	Georgia
Green Rocket	Hale's Best	Enterprise	Freedom	Georgia (or
Joi Choi	Magnum 45	Envy	Graffiti	Creole/Southern)
Mei Quin Choi	Mainstream	Firewedge	Incline	Hi Crop
Michihili	Mission Perlita	Imperator	Majestic	Top Bunch
Monument	Primo	Maverick	Self Blanch	Vates
Rubicon	Royal Sweet	Mokum	Snow Crown	
Yuki	Star Brite	Nantes Fancy	Snowball	
	Uvalde	Navajo	Symphony	
	Vienna	Purple Haze	Veronica Romanesco	
		Scarlet Nantes	Wentworth	
		Sugarsnax 54	Whistler	
		Thumbelina	White Magic	
		Yellowbunch	White Passion	

Corn, Sweet	Cucumbers, Pickling	Cucumbers, Slicing	Eggplant	Garlic
Ambrosia	Boston Pickling	Ashley	Black Beauty	Creole
Avalon	Calypso	Cortez	Black Bell	Elephant
Bodacious	Carolina	Dasher II	Calliope	Italian
Delectable	Eureka	Daytona	Casper	Tahiti
Funks G90	Fancipak	Diva	Classic	
Gold Queen	Homemade Pickles	Fanfare	Cloud Nine	
Golden Cross Bantam	Jackson	General Lee	Dusky	
Golden Queen	National Pickling	Marketmore 76	Epic	
Honey 'N Pearl		Olympian	Fairy Tale	
Honey Select		Poinsett 76	Florida Highbush	
Incredible		Rockingham	Ghostbuster	
Lancelot		Salad Bush	Hansel	
Merit		Slice	Ichiban	
Miracle		Slice More	Kermit	
Precious Gem		Sooyow Nishiki	Nadia	
Seneca Horizon		Spacemaster	Night Shadow	
Silver Queen		Speedway	Orient Express	
White Out		Stonewall	Ping Tung Long	
		Straight Eight	Rosa Bianca	
		Summer Dance	Rosita	
		Suyo Long	Santana	
		Sweet Slice		
		Sweet Success		
		Tasty Green		
		Thunder		

Honeydew Melons	Kale	Lettuce, Cos	Lettuce, Heading	Lettuce, Leaf
Earli-dew	**Blue Knight**	Cimarron Red	Adriana	Black Seeded Simpson
Honey Brew	**Blue Ridge**	Cuore	Buttercrunch	Cherokee
Honey Girl	**Darkibor**	Flashy Trout Back	Caliente	Grand Rapid
Lambkin	Dwarf Blue Curled	Green Forest	Crispino	Green Oak Leaf
Passport	Lacinato (Dinosaur or	Green Towers	Ermosa	Leaf
Sweet Delight	Tuscano	Ideal	Esmeralda	Lolla Rossa
TAM DEW	Red Russian	Jericho	Great Lakes	Nevada
Temptation	Redboor	Musena	Harmony	New Red Fire
	Siberian	Outredgeous	Ithaca	Prizehead
	Starbor	Parris Island Cos	Keeper	Red Oak Leaf
	Winterbor	Red Eye	Manoa	Red Sails
		Ridgeline	Maverick	Red Salad Bowl
		Rouge D'Hiver	Raider	Red Salad Bowl
		Tall Guzman Elite	Skyphos	Red Tango
	Kohlrabi	Tall Guzman Elite	Summer Bibb	Royal Oakleaf
	Early Purple Vienna	Winter Density	Tom Thumb	Ruby
	Early White Vienna			Salad Bowl
	Grand Duke			Sierra
	Rapid Star			Tango
	Winner			Tehama
				Two Star

Mustard Greens	Okra	Onion, Bulbing	Onion, Green	Peas, English
Amara	Annie Oakley	Candy	Beltsville Bunching	Mr. Big
Florida Broadleaf	Burgundy	Contesa	Crystal Wax	Novella II
Green Wave	Cajun Delight	Creole C5	Evergreen White Bunch	Oregon Sugar Pod
Mizuna	Clemson Spineless	Crystal Wax		Oregon Sugar Pod II
Osaka Purple	Cow's Horn	Early Supreme		Sugar Ann
Purple Wave	Emerald	Eclipse	**Shallots**	Sugar Snap
Red Giant	Lee	Granex 33		
Red Giant	Louisiana Green Velvet	Granex 429	Bonheur	
Savannah	North and South	Red Burgundy	Delta Giant	
Southern Giant Curled		Red Creole	Evergreen	
Tatsoi		Red Granex	Louisiana Evergreen	
Tendergreen		Savannah Sweet	Matador	
		Southern Belle	Prisma	
		Texas Grano 1015Y	Summergreen	
		Texas Grano 502		
		Tropicano		

Peas, Southern	Peppers, Chili		Peppers, Sweet	
California No. 5	Anaheim Chile	Jalapeno M	Admiral	Islander
Blackeye	Ancho	Long Red Cayenne	Aladdin	Jackpot
Colossus Crowder	Ancho 101	Long Thin Tula	Aristotle	Jupiter
Dixie Lee Crowder	Big/Giant Chile	Mariachi	Banana Supreme	Keystone Giant
Elite Cream	Cayenne	Mitla	Bell Boy	King Arthur
Hercules Crowder	Charleston Hot	Mitla Jalapeño	Bell Tower	Lafayette
Knuckle Purple Crowder	Chilly Chili	Mucho Nacho Jalapeño	Big Bertha	Lilac
Mississippi Cream	El Rey	NuMex	Biscayne	Marconi
Mississippi Purple Crowder	Garden Salsa Jalapeño	Poblano	Blushing Beauty	Paladin
Mississippi Shipper Crowder	Grande	Red Cherry Bomb	California Wonder	Pimento L
Mississippi Silver Crowder	Habanero	Red Thick Cayenne	Camelot	Plato
Pinkeye Purple Hull	Habanero Caribbean Red	Santa Fe Grande	Capistrano	Purple Beauty
Queen Anne Blackeye	Hatch Chile	Serrano	Carmen	Red Knight
QuickPick Pinkeye	Hildago Serrano	Super Cayenne	Cubanelle	Revolution
Texas No. 8 Cream	Hungarian Hot Wax	Tabasco	Declaration	Stiletto
Top Pick Cream	Inferno	Tam Mild Jalapeño	Emerald Giant	Super Heavyweight
Top Pick Crowder	Jalapeño	Thai	Enterprise	Sweet Banana
Zipper Cream Crowder	Jalapeño El Rey	Tormenta Jalapeño	Excursion	Tequila
			Excursion II	Tiburon Ancho
			Flavorburst	Tiburon Poblano
			Golden Summer	Valencia
			Gypsy	Yolo Wonder
			Heritage	

Potatoes, Irish	Potatoes, Sweet	Pumpkins		
Kennebec	Beauregard	Aladdin	Connecticut Field	Peek a Boo
La Rouge	Bellevue	Appalachian	Darling	Prankster
LaChipper	Bienville	Aspen	Early Abundance	Prize Winner
Norchip	Bonita	Atlantic Giant	Frosty	Silver Moon
Norland	Burgundy	Autumn Gold	Gold Medal	Small Sugar
Purple Majesty	Centennial	Baby Bear	Gold Rush	Sorcerer
Red LaSoda	Evangeline	Baby Boo	Gooligan	Spirit
Red Pontiac	Hernandez	Big Autumn	Howden	Spookie
Yukon Gold	Jewel	Big Max	Jack-Be-Little	Spooktacular
	Murasaki	Big Moon	Jack-O-Lantern	Sunlight
	O'Henry	Casper	Jumpin Jack	Trick or Treat
	Orleans	Charisma	Munchkin	Triple Treat
	Porto Rico	Cinderella	Orange Smoothie	
	Texas Porto Rico			

Radishes	Spinach	Squash, Summer		
Amethyst	Ballet	Ambassador Zucchini	Early Summer	Raven Zucchini
April Cross	Bloomsdale Long Standing	Aristocrat Zucchini	Crookneck	Sebring Zucchini
Bacchus	Melody	Benning's Green Tint	Early White Patty Pan	Spineless Beauty
Black Spanish	Space	Black Beauty Zucchini	Eight Ball Zucchini	Starship Patty Pan
Champion	Tiger Cat	Butterstick Straightneck	Elite	Sunburst Patty Pan
Cherriette	Tyee	Cashflow	Enterprise	Superpik Straightneck
Cherry Belle	Unipack 151	Cocozelle	Straightneck	Superset Crookneck
Chinese White Winter		Cosmos Straightneck	Gentry Crookneck	Sure Thing
Easter Egg		Costata Romanesco	Gold Rush Zucchini	Tatume
Everest Daikon		Dixie Yellow Crookneck	Gold Star Crookneck	Tigress
French Breakfast		Dunja Zucchini	Multipik Straightneck	Zephyr Crookneck
Green Luobo		Early Prolific Straightneck	Payload	
Lo Bok Daikon			Payroll	
Mikura Cross			Peter Pan	
Ping Pong				
Red Satin				
Red Silk				
Rudi				
Scarlet				
Shunkyo				
Snow Belle				
Sparkler				
Watermelon Radish				
White Icicle Daikon				

Squash, Winter		Swiss Chard	Tomatoes, Cherry/Currant	
Bonbon Buttercup	Small Wonder Spaghetti	Bright Lights	Baxter's Early	Smarty
Carnival Acorn	Sunshine Kabocha	Bright Yellow	Black Cherry	Sugar Snack
Cream of the Crop	Sweet Dumpling	Fantasia Orange	Cherry Grande	Sugary
Cushaw Green Striped	Sweet Mama Kabocha	Fordhook Giant	Cupid	Suncherry
Delicata Squash	Table Ace Acorn	Geneva	Gold Nugget	Sungold
Early Butternut	Table King Acorn	Lucullus	Golden Gem	SunSugar
Ebony Acorn	Table Queen Acorn	Magenta Sunset	Husky Cherry Red	Super Sweet 100
Golden Hubbard	Taybelle PM Acorn	Rhubarb	Jolly	Sweet 100
Honey Bear	Tivoli Spaghetti Squash	Ruby Red	Juliet	Sweet Baby Girl
La Estrella Calabaza	Ultra Butternut	Vulcan	Mountain Belle	Sweet Chelsea
Pinnacle Spaghetti	Vegetable Spaghetti		Mountain Magic	Sweet Million
Primavera Spaghetti	Waltham Butternut		Red Cherry	Vita-Gold
			Red Grape	Yellow Cherry
			Small Fry	

Tomatoes, Determinate		Tomatoes, Indeterminate		Tomatoes, Paste
Amelia	Homestead	Arkansas Travel	Green Zebra	Picus Roma
Bella Rosa	Marglobe	Beefmaster	Jaune Flamme	Plum Regal
BHN 444	Mountain Delight	Better Boy	Jet Star	Roma
BHN 602	Mountain Fresh Plus	Big Beef	Jubilee	Royal Chico
Bush Beefsteak	Mountain Pride	Big Dena	Lemon Boy	San Marzano
Carnival	Mountain Spring	Black Krim	Monte Carlo	Spectrum 882
Carolina Gold	Olympic	Brandywine	Mortgage Lifter	Viva Italia
Celebrity	Phoenix	Carbon	Mountain Rouge	
Colonial	Solar Set	Champion	Oaxacan Ribbed	
Floradade	Spitfire	Cherokee Purple	Persimmon	
Floramerica	Talladega	Delicious	Pink Girl	
Florida 47	Tasti Lee	Dona	Pruden's Purple	
Florida 91	Tribeca	Early Girl	Rose de Berne	
Heatwave II	Tycoon	Eva Purple Ball	Stupice	
		Fantastic	Sunray	
		Geronimo	Terrific	
		Goliath	Yellow Pear	
			Zapotec Pleated	

Turnips	Watermelon			
Alamo	Allsweet	Jamboree	Millionaire	Sugar Baby
Just Right	Amarillo	Jubilation	Mirage	Summer Flavor 710
Purple Top	Black Diamond	Jubilee	Moon and Stars	Summer Flavor 720
Seven Top	Buttercup	Jubilee II	Patriot	Summer Gold
Shogoin	Charleston Grey	Juliette	Regency	Tender Gold
Tokyo Cross	Cooperstown	Krispy Krunch	Revolution	Tendersweet
White Lady	Crimson Sweet	La Sweet	Royal Jubilee	Treasure Chest
	Desert King	Liberty	Royal Star	Tri-X 313
	Dixie Lee	Louisiana Sweet	Royal Sweet	Vanessa
	Gold Strike	Matrix	Sangria	
	Gypsy	Mickey Lee	Starbrite	
	Imagination	Millenium	Stars 'N Stripes	

About Southern Garden

Southern Garden is a small, registered nursery in Central Florida. We focus primarily on pollinator plants for bees and butterflies and edible plants for humans, pets, and livestock.

We advocate and practice regenerative growing, with an emphasis on organic and sustainable gardening. Using a blend of permaculture and holistic management, or goal is to live off the land, lessen our impact, and share the joys of protecting the natural world with others.

You can find us online at SouthernGarden.net for seasonal planting updates, profiles on useful plants, and technique and product reviews.

Join us on the gardening journey...

Made in the USA
Coppell, TX
17 February 2023